TO ✓

Florence Nightingale's Nuns

Florence Nightingale's Nuns

by
Emmeline
Garnett

illustrated by Anne Marie Jauss

VISION BOOKS

FARRAR, STRAUS & CUDAHY   NEW YORK
BURNS & OATES   LONDON

Vision Books
is a division of
Farrar, Straus & Cudahy, Inc.
Published simultaneously in Canada by
Ambassador Books, Ltd., Toronto.
Manufactured in the U.S.A.

For Carol

Nihil Obstat:
>   Rt. Rev. Msgr. Peter B. O'Connor
>   *Censor Librorum*

Imprimatur:
>   ✠ Most Reverend Thomas A. Boland, S.T.D.
>   *Archbishop of Newark*

Contents

Author's Note

THE CRIMEAN WAR WAS FOUGHT FROM 1854 to 1856. Russia was on one side, and against Russia were the Allies—Great Britain, France and Turkey. It was an almost pointless war, which seems to have been fought largely because there had been no war in Europe since the battle of Waterloo, and the great powers felt like fighting.

Once Britain and France had declared war, the real problem was how to get at Russia. There were only two ways. One was through the Baltic; a fleet was sent there but it did very little good. The other was through the Black Sea, where there was a great Russian port at Sevastopol in the Crimea.

An Allied army was landed in the Crimea in September 1854. Two brilliant victories, at Alma and Balaclava, followed very quickly, and if the Allies had gone straight on to attack Sevastopol, the city would probably have fallen, and the war would have been over by Christmas. They did not. Instead, they did something incredibly stupid. They besieged the city and settled down to wait until the winter was over.

The story is well known. The British army, without winter clothes, without huts, without ambulances, medicines, firewood or the necessities of life, died on a bare hillside in the grip of a savage winter. It was nobody's fault. It was the fault of forty years of peace and a system so complicated and bound with red tape that on one occasion a shipload of cabbages was thrown into Balaclava harbor while the army was dying of scurvy—because the right forms had not been filled in and so the cargo could not be delivered!

The French and the Russians organized their affairs just as badly. By the time the war staggered slowly to its close, enormous numbers of men had been lost on both sides, comparatively few of them through enemy action.

In the end Sevastopol did fall and the Allies were victorious, but it was a poor sort of victory.

Two people emerged from the war with honor. One was the private soldier, who had proved that he was not what Wellington had called him, "the scum of the earth, enlisted for drink." The other was the hospital nurse.

Nearly everyone knows the story of Florence

Nightingale. If the army in camp was badly treated, there are no words to describe the state of the army hospitals. The story is a sickening and an almost unbelievable one, but it has been told many times, for it is a real fairy story—good triumphs over evil, and the "Lady with the Lamp," that wonderful young woman, works one of the great miracles of the ages.

So often has the story been told, and always with Florence Nightingale as the heroine, that the nurses who went with her are hardly heard of. Few Catholics know that ten Catholic nuns were among the first gallant little band of thirty-eight nurses. Five of them, the ones with whom this story deals, were some of the best nurses and Miss Nightingale's best friends.

The full story of this loyal and devoted little group has not yet been written, and perhaps never will be. Much of my information has come from the Convent of Mercy at Bermondsey, and from the Hospital of St. John and St. Elizabeth. I am very grateful for their help. Of the many books and newspapers I have consulted, all but one are long since out of print, so to make a list of them will not be helpful to the general reader. However, there is in print one magnificent life of Florence Nightingale, which is of the greatest value to anyone interested in this woman and her work.

It is *Florence Nightingale* by Cecil Woodham-Smith (London, 1951).

One last word about how much of this story is invented. All the events are true, even the smallest ones. So is the background. I have not often put in so much as a chair or a table unless I found out that it was actually so. But I have invented conversations. When I knew what people were talking about on a certain occasion, I have put words into their mouths to make the story more lively. And of course I have had to guess at people's thoughts, but I have tried to make my guesses good ones.

These nuns were not the only good and loyal nurses on the expedition. But they were a particularly attractive group, and Miss Nightingale herself said of them: "They are the truest Christians I ever met with, invaluable in their work, devoted, heart and head, to serve God and Mankind."

Florence Nightingale's Nuns

CHAPTER ONE

The Call Comes to Bermondsey

A MAN WAS WALKING THROUGH THE DARK AND noisy streets of London's dockland, when a street Arab, a boy of ten or eleven in filthy rags, dodged out of a dark entry.

"Carry your bag, sir?"

If he hoped for a sixpence, he was due for a disappointment, for this man never let anybody carry things for him if he could help it.

"No, my boy, no, thank you," he said mildly.

"Garn, you ain't no gentleman," spat the urchin, and ran off.

"Perhaps not, my boy, perhaps not," agreed the Bishop of Southwark.

He was walking through part of his bishopric this autumn evening, and a very poor part it was too. The cobbled streets were slushy with mud and dirty with rubbish, and the only gay places were the gin palaces, which were brightly lit with flaring gas jets. Poor people were doing their Saturday night shopping, for pennyworths of stale bread and pennyworths of stale fish and limp green stuff. Most of the children who played in the gutters had no shoes to their feet.

On Saturday evenings Bishop Grant went down to the Convent of Mercy to hear the nuns' confessions. He had made a habit of doing this lately; since Father Butt had gone to the Crimea as an army chaplain, the diocese was rather short of priests. The convent was right down by the Bermondsey waterfront, among cranes and warehouses, and the horrible rabbit warrens called "rookeries" in which so many of his people spent their lives. The Bishop chose to walk; he could not do much for his poor people, but at least he would not bowl through their wretched streets in a comfortable carriage.

The Bishop could not feel particularly happy

walking through Bermondsey, but he was happy when he reached the end of his walk in George Row and rang the polished brass bell that winked at him like an old friend. It was always a joy to step inside this house. It was not a particularly comfortable or handsome one. It was too close to the river, and damp; besides, the architect had had strong feelings on what was the suitable style for a convent, with the result that the narrow pointed windows were set so high that you could not see out of them without standing on a chair. But these things were not so important as the spirit of the place.

Outside in the streets, poverty was dirty and ugly; here, it was clean and beautiful. The board floors were scrubbed so that you could have eaten your dinner anywhere off them. The Sisters' rusty black habits were patched and darned with as much care as though they had been gowns of rich silk. The thing that the Bishop liked best about the convent was that it was a cheerful place. He often said, in his blunt way, that if there was one thing he couldn't abide, it was a gloomy nun. So far he had never met one in Bermondsey.

He was shown into the dark parlor while the portress Sister went to find Reverend Mother. For once, he did not feel exactly comfortable about the coming interview. He paced up and down, and then stopped in front of the cheap white plaster statue of Our Lady and the Holy Child in the corner.

"Our Lady of Mercy, guard us all!" he muttered, but the white madonna's eyes were cast severely downwards, and he felt very much on his own in the decision he was making.

He swung around as the door opened, and immediately gained fresh confidence from the sight of Reverend Mother Mary Clare Moore. Just to see this very remarkable nun was an experience; even from a hundred-year-old photograph her face, rather long, with a broad forehead and very straight heavy black eyebrows, looks out with enormous strength, the strength of complete trust in God. Her other gifts were great intelligence, great kindness, and, rarest of all, quiet.

She had been one of the first seven Sisters of Mercy when the Order was founded some twenty years before in Ireland. The bishop who had received her said: "I never saw so much maturity in one so young." It was not surprising that when the Order founded its first house in London, Sister Mary Clare, although still in her twenties, was chosen to be the first Reverend Mother, and here she had been for the past fifteen years. Under her the Bermondsey house flourished and attracted many young women. It was notable for its good work, but it was especially notable, as many people, both Catholic and Protestant, noticed, for the honest cheerfulness and gaiety which the Sisters spread around them wherever they went.

She kissed the Bishop's ring and waited for him to speak, but it took him a moment to get the words ready.

Then he said, in a kind of a rush, "Reverend Mother, I have important news for you. I have a great deal of work for you and your nuns."

A bright picture swept into her mind, for they had been hoping and praying for new schoolrooms. She thought he must be referring to that. Then the bright picture was blown roughly away.

"I want you to go and nurse the soldiers— in Turkey."

As soon as he had said it, he wished that he could have broken the news more gently.

"My lord, I fear I do not understand you," said Reverend Mother in her usual calm voice, though her hands were clasped so tightly that the knuckles whitened.

On second thought she looked anxiously to see whether it was one of the Bishop's funny stories. Not that the extraordinary statement sounded like a joke; but it did not sound serious either. It was too astonishing.

"I suppose you do not know much about the war, Reverend Mother?"

"Very little," she said. "We do not see the newspapers."

"Then I have a story to tell you."

He made her sit down, which she did, very quietly, on one of the hard, upright chairs. But he paced up and down the room in his excitement—a soldierly little man, whose father had been a sergeant in a Highland regiment, and who had been brought up himself as a regimental baby. He loved soldiers as much as he loved children. When the war broke out he had been appointed Bishop in Ordinary to his beloved army, and he had been working for their good ever since.

He began to tell Reverend Mother Clare the story of the army in the Crimea. He described for her, in bold strong words, the story that the special correspondents' dispatches had been telling in the columns of the London *Times*, the most powerful and outspoken newspaper in the world.

He described, in the glowing words of a soldier rather than a bishop, the battle of the Alma River, at which the French and British armies had soundly beaten the Russians out of a very strong position, at the cost of heavy losses on both sides. Then his voice softened as he told of the death, disease and horror that followed after that victory. The British military hospitals were three hundred miles away, on the other side of the Black Sea, and the so-called hospital ships that carried the wounded had no beds, no bunks, no medical supplies, no doctors. It was forty years since Britain had been at war, and in forty years people had forgotten all they ever knew (they had never known very much) about what to do with the sick and the wounded.

The little Bishop, kindling with anger till the tears stood in his eyes, whipped out a newspaper clipping and began to read it aloud.

"This is an article from the *Times*, published two days ago," he said, and his voice rose higher and higher as he read out the angry words.

"'It is with feelings of surprise and anger that the public will learn that no sufficient preparations have been made for the proper care of the wounded. Not only are there not sufficient surgeons—that, it might be urged, was unavoidable; not only are there no dressers or nurses—that might be a defect of the system for which no one is to blame; but what will be said when it is known that there is not even linen to make bandages for the wounded? . . . Why could not this clearly foreseen want have been supplied? Can it be said that the battle of the Alma has been an event to take the world by surprise? Has not the expedition to the Crimea been the talk of the last four months?

. . . And yet, after the troops have been six months in the country, there is no preparation for the commonest surgical operations! . . . The men must die through the medical staff of the British Army having forgotten that old rags are necessary for the dressing of wounds!'"

He looked at Reverend Mother, expecting a comment.

"This is terrible and shocking," she said, "but—"

"But now," Bishop Grant said, eagerly leaning towards her, "everything is being put to rights, and, please God, the worst is over. There is our great hospital at Scutari, near Constantinople. Many more doctors are being sent out, and shiploads of every sort of medical supplies. All will soon be put right. You know what the Government is—slow to action, but once started, nothing stops them. And stronger than the Government is the feeling of the people of Britain. The Government may send doctors and medicines. But the public is insisting that there should be nurses too."

Reverend Mother sat quite still, no longer puzzled, while from another pocket he produced another piece of newspaper.

"This is from this morning's paper—a letter." He read: "'It is a reproach to us to have made so little provision for our gallant and loved countrymen, while the priests and Convent sisters are doing so much good among the French. It would be well if we could learn from the Roman Catholics the art of making the comforts of religion and the ministry of charity more accessible to all. Why have we no Sisters of Charity? There are numbers of able-bodied and tender-hearted English women who would joyfully and with alacrity go out to devote themselves to nursing the sick and the wounded, if they could be associated for that purpose and placed under proper protection.' Now, Reverend Mother, *now* you know what I want to ask you and your Sisters."

She got to her feet and her eyes shone.

"My lord, if you will come and read those words to them as you have to me, I think you will not be disappointed with your answer."

In the community room the Sisters were sitting in a circle around a long table. The two lamps sent yellow circles of light onto the bent heads and darting needles. They were all sewing, except one, who was mending torn reading books with paste and paper. Two Sisters, one at each end of a long strip of white linen, were drawing threads and hemming with tiny stitches.

"Is that the altar cloth that the Bishop asked for?" said Sister Stanislaus, looking up from a pile of black stockings in which there seemed to be more hole than stocking.

"Yes, it's to go out to Father Butt as soon as it's done, so there's no time for embroidery on it."

"The war" was at that moment as far from the little community as the moon. The only news they heard of it was from the Bishop, news of the priests who had gone as chaplains. The most serious moment of the war for them had been, not the battle of the Alma, but an SOS that the Bishop had sent to Reverend Mother, asking for an altar stone. She had taken the one out of the convent chapel and sent it straight away, and no doubt it was on its way to Constantinople at that moment. The altar stone, and four boxes of books, and the making of the altar linen, and sending out altar breads to the chaplains—they had never considered the possibility of the war coming closer to them than that. And then the door opened, and Reverend Mother came in with Bishop Grant. . . .

The chapel was dark, and the little red flame in the altar lamp seemed to shine like God's own loving care. Confessions were over, and the nuns were saying their prayers for a few minutes longer before going back to the community room to speak to the Bishop again. He had not let them answer him then and there, not till they had prayed about it, for he had insisted that this was a request, not an order, and he would take only volunteers.

For the second time he had told the story of the war, and the Sisters' hands were soon stealing to their rosaries, as though they could not wait to begin praying for the poor soldiers.

"The Cardinal wants a party of Catholic nuns to go," he had said, "and so far the Government has not refused. Nuns are used to discipline. They will work hard, and they will not shrink from the lowest and dirtiest work if it is done for the love of our Lord. This is a wonderful chance to break down the suspicion that many people feel for us and show that if there is work to be done, Catholics are the best people to turn to.

"You may not be needed, but the Cardinal wants eight or ten nuns to be ready and waiting. It has all happened very quickly. I have written to Ireland, but there is no time to wait for their answer. So I have come to ask you."

Reverend Mother had said quietly, not as an excuse, but as a fact:

"We are not nurses, my lord."

"No, Reverend Mother, but you have had some experience during the cholera epidemic, and you will learn."

"What about our work here? We have hardly enough nuns to keep the schools running, and more children come to us every day."

The Bishop had sighed. He loved children.

"I should like to be able to say that the children must come first. But this is a very special kind of emergency. And as to being busy—where is there a convent with half a dozen nuns standing idle? Nuns can never be spared."

"Then we are ready to go wherever we are sent, and we trust you, my lord, not to send us unless it is really necessary." . . .

And now they were sitting in their circle in the community room once more, with Reverend Mother at the end of the table, and the Bishop facing them, with his back to the fireplace.

"I would like to go," said Sister Mary Stanislaus.

"And I, my lord," echoed Sister Anastasia.

Reverend Mother nodded her approval and the Bishop jotted down the names in his notebook. He would have to apply to the Foreign Office for a passport for them.

Sister Stanislaus was a Londoner, and she was thirty-one years old. She had entered the convent when she was twenty-three and had been a valuable member of the community ever since: a plain, practical person, not easily ruffled, and with some experience in nursing cholera, for there had been an epidemic of that fearful disease in Bermondsey this very summer.

Sister Anastasia, a tiny, twinkling little Irishwoman who had nevertheless been born near the London docks where her father, like so many Irishmen, had come to work and escape the famine in his own land, was only twenty-seven, but she had been in the convent longer than most of them. She had entered when she was only fifteen, on a Christmas day twelve years before, having taken it into her head that as she could bring nothing else with her, she would offer herself to the Christ Child as a living Christmas present.

Sister Mary de Chantal, youngest of the community, and not twenty-one till next birthday, spoke next, blushing fiery red, and hesitating a great deal.

"If Reverend Mother—if you please, my lord—"

She was accepted too, and breathed a gusty sigh of relief that made them all smile, solemn though the moment was.

Sister Bridget asked next, pleading, half expecting the answer "no." She had to be refused, on the grounds of ill health.

Reverend Mother waited a moment, looking down the line at Sister Mary Gonzaga's bent head. The merriest, in many ways the most capable, and certainly the stormiest, character in the house evidently felt that she could not volunteer. So after a pause, Reverend Mother spoke for herself.

"Of course, with your permission, my lord, I wish to go too," she said.

As the Bishop left them he said warmly: "I knew that I could depend on my dear Bermondsey convent. I will let you know as soon as I can what has been decided."

Next morning, after Mass, Reverend Mother Mary Clare was tidying her desk and writing letters. If they had to set out at short notice, the convent business must be all tidy and up to date; if not—well, it never hurt a desk to be in order, she thought, smiling to herself as she tied papers in neat bundles and wrote notes on the outside.

There was a knock on the door. It was Sister Gonzaga. For one who usually had no difficulty in saying what she meant, and indeed was apt to err on the side of saying too much rather than too little, she was tongue-tied and acutely embarrassed. Always pale, this morning she had no color whatever and her face was drawn as though she had not slept at all—which was probably true, thought Reverend Mother, who knew how much she took things to heart.

"Reverend Mother."

"Yes, Sister, what can I do?"

Another stammer and a false start, and then Reverend Mother took pity and helped her out. It did not take long to tell; acutely aware of her own faults and difficulties, and the fact that she had no experience in nursing, she had not dared to volunteer, although longing to do so. Now, after a sleepless night, although prepared for refusal, she felt she had at least to ask and see what happened.

"You were right to feel cautious, Sister. Anyone who goes will have to guard herself very carefully for fear of giving scandal. On the other hand, it seems to me that the first thing we shall need will be cheerfulness, and you usually can provide a never-ending supply of *that*."

She smiled at the young nun's anxious face until it suddenly relaxed and Sister Gonzaga beamed at her.

"You mean—you *wish* me to volunteer?"

Ten minutes later, seated at the community room table, with her heart as joyous as a bird, she was preparing to write a letter to the Bishop, adding her own name to the list of volunteers.

My lord, she wrote, and then found her hand so shaking with excitement that she had to wait a moment before going on.

She looked up at the blank wall, and it melted away, showing her a distant view of hardship and hunger, tossing seas and cruel lands.

She was one of those people who longs to do everything, dare everything, give everything.

Giving never seemed hard. It was the small things in life that she found hard, like curbing her tongue when something appealed to her keen wit. People thought that she had given up everything when she became a Catholic, and then again when she had given up a wealthy home at the age of twenty-two, cut off her lovely hair and hidden her good looks under a nun's veil. Each time it had been joyfully easy; perhaps this time God was asking something more difficult. She hoped so.

"But only one thing could really be hard," she said to herself as she took up her pen again: *Reverend Mother has given me permission to write to you.* "The only really hard thing would be to hear on Monday that we are not wanted after all."

Florence Nightingale

CHAPTER TWO

Miss Nightingale's Nurses

By Monday morning the whole scheme seemed distant and dreamlike, and even Sister Mary Gonzaga, coming back from the schoolroom at dinnertime, had her mind full of her little barefoot Pats and Biddies rather than the war. But Reverend Mother was waiting to read them a note she had had from the Bishop:

"I do not know if there is any hope of success, but provide warm clothing for four and have them ready if they are allowed to go."

She was in the middle of reading this aloud when the doorbell rang again, and there was another messenger with a fat envelope, sealed with the Southwark seal.

Sister Gonzaga held her breath as, in a hush that could be felt, Reverend Mother tore open the packet and took out what was inside. First there was a thick and beautifully scripted document—a passport. How many names were on it? The clouds cleared as Sister Gonzaga heard her own read out. So she was to go after all! She dragged her attention back to the Bishop's letter which Reverend Mother was reading aloud.

"My dear daughters in Christ,
In times of real difficulty the daughters of Mary must be ready to imitate her in her journey with haste into the mountains. Five of your number must start for Turkey to-morrow to nurse the sick. Our dear Mother will guard those who remain, and as the lot of those who go will be more difficult, it is necessary for her sake that your Reverend Mother should be one of the five.

"May our Dear Lord guard and guide you all,

†Thomas Grant."

People are very good at pretending that unpleasant things are not going to happen, and several of the Sisters who were to stay behind were as horrified by this letter as though it were the first news they had had. The thought of losing Reverend Mother was the worst blow, for life in the hostile England of 1854 was not easy for nuns. The Sisters did not even wear their habits in the street, for fear of trouble, but disguised themselves under plain bonnets and shawls as they went about their work.

Poor little Sister Bridget went back to school in the afternoon to take a double class, her own and Sister Gonzaga's, and halfway through the first lesson she fairly broke down and cried. Whereupon all the little girls cried in sympathy; and when she tried to tell them what was the matter, and ask them to pray hard for the Sisters who were going, they only howled the louder, half in sadness and half in fright. Most of them had never heard of Turkey before, and it sounded as far away and as dangerous as a trip to the moon.

Meanwhile the convent was in turmoil too, though not quite so noisily. The parting was bad enough, at such short notice, but it was impossible to foresee when, or if ever, Reverend Mother Clare and her four companions would see George Row again.

"When—what time—do you—?" Sister Mary

Aloysius, who tomorrow would be the acting
head of the little community, tried to get the
question out.

"Ten minutes past eight at London Bridge
station," said Reverend Mother, and to all of
them it sounded like a death sentence. The
cook Sister retired to the kitchen and wept
into the pots as she tried to make something
extra nice for supper. It was a wasted effort as
nobody felt hungry anyway.

The five who were going had to be fitted
out with the warmest and best clothes. There
was much mending and patching and trying on,
much sorting out of the best and strongest
boots that might fit the travelers, much hasty
writing of letters and looking for things that
had gone astray. They had not much time for
feeling miserable, although a shadow was on
them all. It was only a poor and trembling
laugh that they could raise at Sister Gonzaga's
jokes about the ill-assorted garments they were
to wear.

There was one great comfort—they were to
travel in their habits. On this important occasion all the world must know that they were
nuns and proud of it.

The convent doorbell never seemed to stop
ringing that evening. First it was Father Collingridge, who came from the Bishop with the
money they were to take. He looked with a

sort of sad wonder at the five little piles of luggage on the table. Each pile consisted of a few underclothes, handkerchiefs, caps, and a prayer book or two. The Sisters had only one habit each, the one they wore.

The chaplains who had gone out had not been exactly wealthy, but their luggage had run to stout boxes, nailed and corded. These women apparently intended to tuck paper parcels under their arms.

He went off to the shops and bought five railway rugs and five little holdalls, and when he came back with these things, there was another visitor. This time it was the Bishop.

He was brisk and practical as ever, hiding his feelings behind an air of cheerfulness. He brought more money, instructions, letters of introduction to various people who might be useful. He gave them the name of a Paris hotel where they could stay, and promised to send them full instructions as to their next step.

"Things are moving so rapidly in Government circles," he said, "that plans are made and changed from day to day. In any case, wait a day or two in Paris, and see what happens. You will probably be joined by some nuns from Ireland."

But when all the practical advice was over, and the time came to say good-by, Reverend Mother said:

"Have you any other words of advice for us, my lord, at the beginning of our journey?"

She was calm and quiet as ever, but he suddenly found that the words stuck in his throat and he could say nothing. He looked around, shook his head, and muttered, "Nothing, nothing—just do the best you can."

Then, sketching a blessing in the air over them all, he hurried out of the house as though he could not even trust himself to say good-by.

London Bridge station next morning was grey and cold. It was barely light when the five travelers, escorted by Father Collingridge, gathered to wait for the train. A few curious glances were given to their habits, but the railway officials were polite enough and found them an empty second-class carriage. They would have been more curious and even more polite if they had known where the expedition was bound to. There was nothing to suggest Turkey, however, in the five women with their little handbags, their rugs and their umbrellas, waiting for the eight-ten train.

All at once there was a great deal of whistling and banging of doors, and quite suddenly the train started. Sister Mary de Chantal, sitting in the corner with her back to the engine, saw Father Collingridge for a moment or two, standing with his hat off and getting smaller and smaller. Then there was nothing but the cranes and warehouses and mean streets.

"Oh," she cried suddenly, "there's the *convent!*"

They had forgotten that as the railway ran down to Greenwich on arches, they would be able to see over the tops of the houses, and there, sure enough, was the church and the convent. They jumped up and gazed out of the window as long as the last little bit of the roof was visible, and when they sat down again, for the first time they seemed to realize what a terrible demand obedience was making on them, and a wave of homesickness came over them all.

After a while Reverend Mother said, "There are five of us, and we are going on a mission to be the hands and feet of our dear Lord. Let us dedicate ourselves to His Five Wounds."

They forgot their troubles as they wrote on slips of paper and drew lots. Reverend Mother drew the Wound of the Right Hand, Sister Gonzaga that of the Left Hand; it was a simple little piece of piety that appealed to them, for they were not complicated people. But we can look ahead at the rest of the story and see that there was something symbolic about it too. They were to represent the Hands and the Feet and the loving Heart of Christ to a great

many people before they saw London Bridge
station again.

Twenty-four hours later, Reverend Mother
Mary Clare stood by a hotel window and
looked out at the roofs of Paris. She and Sister
Gonzaga had been out early for Mass, leaving
the others to rest. The maid had brought in a
pot of hot coffee and a basket of rolls straight
from the baker's. It was a real holiday breakfast, and after her early walk Reverend Mother
was so hungry that while waiting for the others
she turned her back and thought about their
journey.

In London one of the priests had asked
anxiously: "Who is to escort you? You can't
go alone like that!" And she had turned it into
a joke, saying that as far as she knew her
guardian angel had volunteered for the job.
Last night, however, it had really looked as
though her guardian angel had a very poor
knowledge of Paris.

They had arrived late, taken a cab to the
hotel the Bishop had recommended, only to
find it full and the proprietor dismissing them
with shrugs of his shoulders.

Paris suddenly seemed enormous and hostile.
There must be hundreds of hotels, but what
was the use of hundreds when you did not
know which to choose? The nuns had clustered
around, lonely and frightened, and Reverend

Mother had had to summon up her courage and think for them all.

"It's quite simple," she had said with more assurance than she felt. "We'll go to the Bishop's friend and ask his advice."

She could afford to smile now at the awful moment that had followed, when they had roused the *concierge*, using their umbrella handles on the stout wooden door, and he, flourishing his watch and pointing to the hands that said midnight, had refused, in floods of rapid French, to wake up Mr. Goldsmid.

Reverend Mother and Sister Gonzaga both spoke quite good French, and they had pleaded, one on each side of the man. It had no effect. If they had been a little wiser in the ways of the world and tried a few francs as an argument, things might have been different. However, the man had softened in the end. Or perhaps, thought Reverend Mother with a smile, he had merely been appalled at the thought of five strange *Soeurs de Charité* camping on his doorstep. At any rate he had shown them this hotel at the end of the street, and here they were, the first hurdle over, and a few hundred miles nearer to Turkey.

The others came, and coffee had been poured, when the maid came back and announced a gentleman, who almost rushed in, trouble on his kindly face, and his hand stretched out to shake theirs.

"I came as soon as they told me you were here," he said, not waiting to introduce himself. "To think that they turned you away at midnight! But are you all right? Are you *sure* you're all right?"

It was Mr. Goldsmid himself, and in the days that followed the nuns felt that if he had been the brother of them all they could not have been better looked after.

That first morning he brought them a telegram from London, sent after they left, to say that they were to await further instructions. So they enjoyed what was really a week's holiday in Paris. They saw most of the famous buildings and went to Mass at different churches. They went to see the Sisters of Charity at St. Roch's Hospital, who gave them a great many useful hints about their work, and they spent some of the Bishop's money on medical supplies which might be useful.

"Of course," said Reverend Mother, when the cases of shining surgical instruments were sent home to the hotel, and they all stood around, unpacking and admiring, "no doubt by the time we reach Scutari, the early troubles will be over, and there will be no lack of supplies. Still, to be prepared for the worst is always a good thing."

Sunday was the fifth day of their stay in Paris, and Reverend Mother wrote to the Sisters at Bermondsey. She had much to say, for letters had been going backwards and forwards since they arrived, and that very morning she had heard from the Bishop that they were no longer to be on their own, but were to join a much larger party of nurses, led by a lady whom they had never heard of before, but who the Bishop assured them was entirely to be trusted—a Miss Nightingale.

"Dear Mother Aloysius and Sisters," she wrote. "As the time of our departure is now fixed I shall begin a letter and I think if you write on the 29th we shall be at Scutari in time to receive your letter. There will be more than forty if any of the French Sisters of Charity can be obtained, otherwise only about thirty-six, of whom ten will be nuns, including ourselves.

"Here we are very happy and merry and pious enough, as we have two Masses and benediction daily. I have been thinking very much of you all. . . ."

She looked up and sighed. There was so much ahead that was unknown. Not only the work and the hardships: those were fairly straightforward. But how would they manage in the mixed company of hospital nurses, nuns from other Orders, Anglican Sisters? They had all lived together for years. Even little Sister de Chantal, at this moment crouched over her letter home in a familiar position, had been in the convent for four years. They thought alike, shared the same work, were bound by the same rules and regulations. She took up her pen again:

"Now pray that we may do everything very well and give great satisfaction. Try to keep all at Bermondsey well and happy—Sisters, children and all. I have you all within my heart. . . ."

She pushed the letter away a second time as the French chambermaid came in to announce to *ma mère* that there was a lady to see her. The nuns saw, standing in the doorway, one of the most striking women they had ever seen— tall, slim, graceful. She was younger than Reverend Mother, though older than the rest of them, about thirty-five. Her very plain black dress and bonnet only served to set off her pale oval face and dark hair and the powerfully attractive look of one who has suffered and overcome suffering, who knows exactly what she is doing and why.

"How do you do. I am Florence Nightingale."

They knew it could not be anyone else, for this was a woman who would most certainly get things done, and they trusted her at first sight.

If they were impressed by their Lady Superintendent, she was impressed on her side too. In spite of the popular clamor for nurses, it had been almost impossible to find thirty or forty suitable women, and Miss Nightingale felt that she had brought to Paris a very motley collection. She was used to judging people, and as she looked from Sister de Chantal's enthusiastic rosy face to Sister Gonzaga's pale and beautiful one, from Sister Anastasia, perky as a bird, to Sister Stanislaus, all capable common sense, she felt without doubt that here at least were some of the right sort. And then she turned again to Reverend Mother Clare, in whose dark gray eyes and wonderful air of serenity she recognized a woman of strength as great as her own.

Impulsively she held out her hand, and her charming smile took them all in.

"I cannot tell you, Reverend Mother," she said, "how glad I am to have you and your nuns with me in this expedition."

"We have little nursing experience, as you know, Miss Nightingale, but with God's help we can assure you of loyalty and hard work."

It was the beginning of a strange strong friendship between two remarkable people.

The story of "The Female Nursing Establishment of the English General Hospitals in Turkey," as it was solemnly called, was to be one of trouble. Miss Nightingale often stood alone, surrounded, not only by the terrible difficulties of her job, but by quarrels and mistrust and plots and plans and hatred. She was never quite alone though. Although much of the trouble would arise from religious differences, she could always count absolutely on the unselfish loyalty of the nuns from Bermondsey, and the friendship of Reverend Mother Clare was a comfort to her until they were separated by death.

All this was in the future. On that Sunday morning, October 22nd, 1854, none of them knew what was coming to them. But as the door closed behind Miss Nightingale after a pleasant visit, Sister de Chantal spoke for them all with a gusty sigh:

"Isn't she *wonderful?*"

CHAPTER THREE

A Stormy Passage

THE "VECTIS" LAY BESIDE THE QUAY, A small snub-nosed steamer with huge round paddle boxes quite out of proportion to the rest of her. A stream of black smoke flowed from her tall, thin funnel across the evening landscape, showing that she was ready to put to sea.

A strange procession of women lined up raggedly on the edge of the quay to look down on their next means of transportation, and the

Marseilles fishermen could be heard guessing loudly as to what these people might be.

Sister Mary Gonzaga stood at the end of the line, and with her usual eye for the ridiculous, smiled at herself and her companions. They were an odd collection, indeed.

Miss Nightingale had gone aboard earlier in the day to persuade the captain that she had been delayed quite long enough on her journey already, and he must set sail that evening, Friday or not. In the end he had agreed, but not without a good deal of grumbling. The passengers were headed by Mr. and Mrs. Bracebridge, Miss Nightingale's friends. They were goodhearted people or they would hardly have agreed to accompany her to Turkey, but they could not help being a little ridiculous. Mr. Bracebridge dashed about like an enthusiastic collie with a rather stupid mob of sheep, and never let go of the box under his arm which contained all the expedition's money. At home he had been a major in the yeomanry, and he plainly thought that a little military discipline would have been a great advantage in dealing with all these unruly women.

Miss Nightingale's other friend on the expedition was stout Mrs. Clark. She had come out as cook and general factotum, and told everybody what she thought of them, but her bark was much worse than her bite. She disapproved thoroughly of the Popish religion, but she had conceived a great admiration for Reverend Mother which she tried to hide. In fact, rather against her will, the five Bermondsey nuns were already favorites of hers; there was no nonsense about them, and they laughed when small things went wrong.

Hers was not the only heart that the Bermondsey nuns had won. They received puzzled and fascinated glances from some of the Anglican Sisters. There were eight of these, from different houses of a Sisterhood called "Sellonites" after their foundress. They had learned to think of a convent as a cold, miserable place, with very little of the warmth that comes from love. Their last instructions from Miss Sellon had been: "Observe silence among yourselves, and if persons speak to you, reply shortly, but courteously. Do not converse with anyone excepting Miss Nightingale, and not with her during your silence time." But two of the youngest and liveliest, Sister Elizabeth and Sister Sarah, had already decided that circumstances alter cases, and took every opportunity to talk to the Bermondsey nuns, particularly Sister Gonzaga, whose sense of humor delighted them.

They exchanged glances with her now, and their eyes twinkled, as the hospital nurses were helped aboard, with some difficulty. Most of these good women were elderly and stout, for

Miss Nightingale wanted only the thoroughly respectable. They were dressed in uniforms which had been hastily made to a pattern and handed out, and were too short for some and too long for others. The uniform was an ugly thing, a long grey tweed dress, rather shapeless, a white cap, brown bonnet, and a brown scarf worn over one shoulder and under the other, with "Scutari Hospital" embroidered across it in scarlet letters. The nurses looked anything but elegant, as, clutching their umbrellas and portmanteaux, they were helped aboard by a sailor who looked as gloomy as they did.

"Friday!" Sister Gonzaga heard him mutter as he gave her his enormous fist to steady her. "Friday! We has to set sail on *Friday* and with women aboard!"

He spat into the Mediterranean to show his disgust.

"Black ones," he grumbled, looking at the passengers' clothing, "and white ones. And grey ones tied up with ribbon. Lord! And on a Friday, on the wettest old tub I ever cast my eye on."

The last ones aboard were the five "white" Sisters. These were Catholic nuns from an orphanage in South London, the Convent of the Faithful Virgin at Norwood. Poor things, they looked extremely anxious. For them, this trip was undertaken out of pure charity. They

had no experience of nursing, and, as they ran
an orphanage and hardly ever went outside the
convent grounds, they had no experience of
the world either.

When the Bishop came down to visit them
two days after the Bermondsey nuns had left
for Paris, he told the Reverend Mother that he
was worried. He was allowed by the Government to send ten Catholic nuns with the Crimean expedition; five had gone, but he had had
no answer from the Irish convents.

The Reverend Mother rose to the occasion.

"We are not nurses, my lord," she said, "but
if you need us—"

So here they were, frightened but resolute.
The youngest of them, Sister St. George, confessed later that she fainted at the sight of a
cut finger!

Miss Nightingale came to the group as they
stood nervously on the deck, feeling the movement under their feet as the engines throbbed.

"You are all to be berthed in the forecabin,"
she said briskly. "This sailor will show you the
way."

The gloomy sailor ducked and pulled his
forelock, and led the party along the deck.

"This 'ere's the forecabin," he announced
with something like enjoyment, as he led them
towards a hole in the deck and a steep wooden
ladder leading downwards.

They went down. For a moment even the most talkative of the nurses, even Mrs. Clark, were shocked into silence.

"*Well!*" said one of them at last.

Another, exploring a little further, let out an alarmed squeak.

"*Bugs!*" she said.

"And cockroaches!" cried another, for their approach had startled scores of the creatures, which were scampering in all directions on the boards of the bunks.

They had been allotted the bow end of the ship, a dark hole usually used only for mail-bags, but in these unusual circumstances forty women had to be stowed here. It was all tiny, black, bare, hideously uncomfortable. The poor Sellonites came off worst, as they were allotted the eight bunks in the forepeak. It did not need much imagination to think how they would feel the movement of the ship if the weather turned rough.

The Catholic nuns came off best, after a fashion, for their bunks had been hastily constructed by the ship's carpenter at the bottom of the ladder leading to the deck. There were cockroaches, but no bugs, and it was neither so dark nor so lively as the other end of the quarters.

Sister Gonzaga slowly undid her bag, put

her umbrella on a nail, and spread her traveling rug on the bunk allotted to her.

"This is the best place," she said to Reverend Mother in a low voice. "I wish we could offer it to some of the others."

"Best place, says you, ma'am?" Their sailor friend paused halfway up the ladder. "You wait till a wave or so comes aboard, ma'am!"

"I'm sure it is the best, though," said Sister Gonzaga when he had gone. "I'm sure a wetting with good clean sea-water is much more pleasant than all those creatures."

They could hear the nurses next door conducting a vigorous hunt for the "creatures." There were slaps and bangs and cries of disgust, and presently Mrs. Clark's calm voice:

"Well, my dears, you can kill 'em if you like. It's all according to whether you prefer the bite of a live bug or the smell of a dead one."

For three days the little steamer fairly walked through the Mediterranean waves, her paddle-wheels threshing, and the engine throb-throbbing as she ate up the miles, trailing her banner of black smoke behind her. Those who were not ill spent most of the time on deck, and the white spray blew in their faces, encrusting their clothes with sparkling salt. In spite of the cold, several of the nurses, particularly the two young Sellonite Sisters, spent days and nights on deck, preferring it to the horrible stuffy darkness below.

Some were really ill, and to these the journey was sheer horror because there was no relief. The little ship pitched like a cork, and they lay utterly exhausted on the hard boards, unable to eat, unable to sleep, unable to breathe fresh air.

To the sufferers Sister Gonzaga was chief nurse. With her skirts kilted she ran up and down the wooden ladder, working off her high spirits by turning herself into a maid of all work. It was she who brought mugs of tea and propped up the sick to drink it, told them cheerful stories of the speed at which the *Vectis* was covering the miles, offered the help of an arm if they wanted to stagger on deck, or the loan of a rug if they preferred to stay where they were.

But even she lost her cheerfulness each time she passed the bunk where Reverend Mother lay flat on the boards, eyes shut, too feeble even to turn her head, though you could see from the movement of her lips that she was conscious and praying.

Sister Gonzaga drew Mrs. Roberts aside one day for comfort, because she had been a nurse in a London hospital for more than twenty-five years.

"Do people die of seasickness?" she asked anxiously.

But Mrs. Roberts was skilled in surgical cases, not seasickness, and she shook her head and didn't know. The nuns were frightened, Sister Gonzaga most of all. The future did not bear thinking about without Reverend Mother, the one absolutely reliable point in a shifting world. If they would only reach Malta, where the boat would stand still for a few hours. . . .

"Shore party! Shore party! Boat's waiting alongside, ma'am."

A sailor put his head through the hatch and bawled. Mr. Bracebridge had undertaken to conduct the party, and he was waiting in the boat, fussy and important. Seventeen nuns and nurses decided to go. The others preferred to stay behind and rest quietly, making up the sleep they had lost since Marseilles.

There was only one casualty on the way ashore, a stout old body who slipped between the rowing boat and the shore and went in head first. Luckily the water was shallow, and only her dignity was hurt.

Mr. Bracebridge marshalled the rest of them into a crocodile.

"Black Sisters in front, please," he said briskly, "white Sisters at the rear, nurses in the middle. Now, ready, ladies? Then—forward!"

"I suppose he thinks that nuns are more easily disciplined," said Sister Gonzaga to the "black Sister" beside her, who happened to be a Sellonite, as they set off.

Soon a crowd gathered around the embarrassed women as they straggled up the steep streets from the harbor. Mr. Bracebridge did not seem to mind the publicity at all, and as he pushed importantly through the narrow streets, he announced to all and sundry, Maltese loiterers, British and French troops, who were looking on with great amusement:

"Make way please! These ladies are the Sisters and nurses, going out to nurse the soldiers."

"Mr. Bracebridge's religious yeomanry!" said Sister Gonzaga to her companion, who laughed and said that she hoped there was no special correspondent of *Punch* magazine among the crowds, or they would be the subject of next week's cartoon.

Embarrassment was forgotten when they entered the Cathedral of the Knights of St. John. Peace came down on them by contrast with the dusty glare outside. All around were the calm carved effigies of old knights, above their heads a wonderful painted roof, and in the distance the familiar light of candles, and a figure in crimson and white. A priest was saying Mass, and thankfully the Catholic nuns fell on their knees.

Mr. Bracebridge would not let them stay until the end, but lined up his religious yeomanry again outside the cathedral.

"Halt! To the right face! Advance!" he shouted. He was perturbed to find that his flock did not respond very easily to military orders.

"Those wretched white Sisters have gone again," he was heard to mutter.

"Those there ancient Amazons we read about, Tom," observed a British sergeant to his companion, "must have took a deal of drilling."

But the visit to Malta was all too short. That very night the *Vectis*, with more coal aboard and moving full steam ahead to be in time with the mail at Constantinople, ran out of harbor into the teeth of an autumn gale.

Even the best sailors were ill now. Sister Sarah, unable to stay on deck any longer, and staggering to her bunk in the forepeak, noticed that even Sister Gonzaga was down, lying like a statue, her eyes tightly shut so as not to see the swinging of the cabin lamp. Her pale face (which looked, thought Sarah, so remarkably like a beautifully carved saint's until you caught the restless twinkle in her eyes, when she looked extremely human after all) was upturned to the cabin roof a few inches above her nose.

By morning she was up and about again, and
back to her self-appointed task of nursing the
others. She had a tonic effect on most of them,
though some could not help suspecting that
she was actually enjoying herself. Mrs. Clark
hinted something of the sort.

"I'm sorry," Sister Gonzaga said, contritely.
"Still, it is a great adventure, isn't it?"

"It'll be a great adventure if we all end up
on the bottom of the sea," said Mrs. Clark
grimly.

"Reverend Mother has promised five Masses
for the holy souls when we get to Scutari,"
said Sister Gonzaga with calm conviction.
"You'll see, the wind will go down soon."

"Well, now, that beats all," said Mrs. Clark
to no one in particular, shrugging her shoulders
at the ways of papists. "Breakfast time—who's
a-coming down to have the coffee spilt over
theirselves? Oh, my word, that was a wild
one!"

The ship shuddered from end to end.

"No breakfast," said Sister de Chantal, clutching at Sister Gonzaga. "I'm far too frightened
to eat."

All that day and into the night the gale
raged. The hatch over the forecabin was bat-
tened down at nightfall. Just before the last
of the fresh air disappeared, the first mate put
his head down.

"You'll be good, won't you?" he called cheerfully. "I'm afraid it will be a noisy night, and we shall have our hands full."

They tried to keep their promise, but at midnight there was a sudden fearful bang, like nothing they had heard before, and then silence. Water poured through the hatch-covers.

"We're going down! She's hit a rock! She's settling!"

Indeed the movement, like a horse leaping and leaping at a wall that it never cleared, had changed to something slower and heavier. A few minutes before, they had thought that all they wanted in the world was for that awful movement to cease. Now the comparative quiet was more terrifying still.

They leaped up fearfully, and those who were undressed tried to drag on their clothes in the dark. There were shouts, thumps, dragging noises overhead. One of the nurses began to scream:

"They're getting the boats out! The ship's going down! Oh, God save us!"

There was uproar down below, and like all terrible moments it was partly comic. One of the nurses flopped on her knees and began to pray loudly in Welsh. Then she stopped to say to the others, "Indeed, it's a pity that you cannot understand the beautiful words that I am saying."

At last, above, the watchbell rang out comfortingly, and a voice cried, dying into the fearful noises of the night, "All's we-e-e-ll!"

The ship began to pitch again with the old familiar movement. They were not going to drown this time.

But then Mrs. Clark, that kind, comfortable, sensible woman, lost her temper. She picked up a stool and in a fury began to pound at the deck over her head, bellowing like a bull. It was not for herself that she was so furious.

"Stop the ship!" she roared. "STOP THIS SHIP!! I'm not having any more of it. Slow down her pace. You'll kill all these women. Stop-the-ship-and-*let-us-out!*"

It worked. In answer to this hullabaloo an officer appeared and looked quite shocked at the scene that met his eyes. He went away and presently the captain came down. Then a sailor was sent for to mop up the swashing water in which many of the women were lying like pale bundles of rags, half drowned and half dead with weariness.

The sailor was the same one who had helped them aboard, so long ago.

"What did we hit?" someone asked him nervously.

"Nothing but a lot of water, ma'am, but that's one of the hardest things in the world. She gets her bit in her teeth, this ship, and just bores through it. Won't ride at all. That last lot put the fires out, that's what happened."

He wrung his mop finally into the bucket and went up the ladder. Sister Gonzaga followed him a little way to look out, and came back with the good news that dawn was breaking and that the steward was coming with a bucket of coffee for them. She kept to herself the fact that the deck looked very peculiar in the half-light. The deck cabins had all been washed overboard by that last tremendous crash.

The worst was over. Exhausted, dirty, damp, hungry, some of the passengers wished that they had never come, but most felt considerable pride in the dangers and hardships they had passed.

Even Reverend Mother, though very pale and worn, was on deck next morning to see land. Across a waste of grey sea, through a fine drizzle that was more like England than the "glorious East," there it was, like a faded photograph of painted houses, domed mosques, spiky minarets—Constantinople.

"There can't be anything worse ahead than what we've been through," someone said with great relief.

But there was.

CHAPTER FOUR

First Look at Scutari

ON ONE SIDE OF THE NARROW STRAIT CALLED
the Bosphorus loomed Constantinople, that
crowded city of the East. But it was to the
other side, to the suburb of Scutari, that the
nurses looked.

Presently the sun came out, and the captain
pointed out for them what they were looking
for.

"There's your hospital, Miss Nightingale,"
he said. The Lady Superintendent, like several

others, was on deck for the first time since leaving Marseilles, for she was a wretched sailor.

Rising above the roofs, set high on a hill above the sea, looking white and splendid in the sudden gleam of sunlight, the Turkish Barracks was a most impressive sight.

Each side of the huge square building was a quarter of a mile long, with a tower at each corner. At the back, because of the slope of the ground, it was fairly low, but in front it was three or four stories high. It had been built to house an immense number of Turkish troops, but the Turks had handed it over to their allies as a hospital.

While the captain told them as many facts about its size as he could remember, the eyes of every one of the band of women were fixed on its distant outline, fascinated and somewhat appalled too.

"Oh, dear Miss Nightingale," murmured one of the more sentimental voices among them earnestly, "don't let any red tape get in the way. Let us get to nurse the poor fellows at once."

"The strongest of you," was the somewhat crushing answer, "will be wanted at the wash tub, I have no doubt."

Already distressing rumors were coming to her ears from across the water about the state

of things in that immense palace. People came
and went and were taken down to the cabin,
or walked with Miss Nightingale on the deck.
The "caiques," the little gondolas of the Bosphorus, swarmed round the *Vectis*, but the
nurses, impatient to be on shore, soon tired of
watching the picturesque Turkish boatmen. A
grand, official-looking gentleman arrived from
the British Embassy. The mailbags were un-
packed. The customs men arrived. Out in the
roadstead a British ship from the Crimea was
unloading wounded soldiers into caiques, and
the sailors soon heard, by some sort of bush
telegraph, the news of the second great battle
of the war, Balaclava, news which they passed
on to the nurses.

The Bermondsey nuns retired to their cabin
to say their office, not forgetting particular
thanks to Our Lady of Mercy for bringing
them safely across the stormy water.

An interruption came in the shape of a
message from the aftercabin:

"Miss Nightingale's compliments to the Reverend Mother Bermondsey and would she be
kind enough to step aft."

Reverend Mother went, leaving the others to
finish their prayers and then to wonder about
their disembarkation and to talk about their
future work with a mixture of fear and excitement. What was that distant Barrack like?

Were the terrible things they had heard about it, still true? They exchanged such scraps of information and guesswork as they had, going around and around the same facts, as people do when a subject is of such painful interest that they cannot leave it alone.

Meanwhile Reverend Mother found Miss Nightingale resting on a couch in the after-saloon. She looked tired, but she was talking gaily to the captain.

"I'm just saying to the captain," she said with a smile to Reverend Mother, "that he did not keep his threat. I thought we were all to be drowned for daring to set sail on a Friday."

The captain bowed gallantly to Mother Mary Clare as he went back to his cabin.

"So of course we should have been," he said, "but the Sisters' prayers kept us afloat."

"I asked you to come, Reverend Mother," said Miss Nightingale when they were alone, "because I have had a message from the convent in Constantinople, that should you and your Sisters wish to pay them a visit to recover from the effects of the voyage they would be very glad to have you."

Reverend Mother's straight black brows raised themselves a trifle.

"The Norwood nuns have decided to take advantage of the offer," added Miss Nightingale. "I shall not conceal from you," she went on, "that there will probably be many delays and disappointments in our settling to work here. You need not think that you will be deserting your post by taking a little holiday first."

"We have come out as your nurses," said Reverend Mother, "and if you are going straight to the hospital, we would rather go with you."

Miss Nightingale straightened herself a little as though in a day of disappointments, this was one burden the less.

"Besides," added Reverend Mother Clare with that straight look which concealed a twinkle, "my Sisters have conceived such an admiration for their chief that I do not think I could persuade them."

"Strange things happen," said Miss Nightingale suddenly. "The strangest of all seems to me, Reverend Mother, that *I* am here as your chief, and not *you* as mine."

Later that afternoon a procession of black caiques, rowed by dirty and picturesque Turkish watermen, left the *Vectis* and paddled like a row of waterbeetles towards the Scutari shore.

Sister Anastasia, sharing one with Reverend Mother, giggled suddenly from her place on the comfortable cushions. "It's just exactly as we used to take an afternoon's outing to Greenwich when I was a child," she said.

But the smile died suddenly as the smell of

the shore came out to meet them. Their caique
almost bumped into a bloated thing, rolling
in the waves. It was the carcass of a horse,
with its legs sticking out like ninepins. The
horrible object rolled and washed in the surf
only a few yards from the jetty, chased by a
howling pack of dogs which snapped at it and
each other.

Sister Anastasia forgot about Greenwich. She
turned her eyes away as the boatman helped
her onto the rickety jetty, and in doing so
she looked straight into another caique unloading on the other side. Lying in the bottom
were two muddy bundles of rags which had
been men. One had his eyes tightly shut, but
the other looked straight at her from under a
bloodstained bandage. The skin was drawn so
tight over his skull-like face that you wondered
why the bones had not worn holes in it. For
the first time she understood that war was
real.

They were all quite silent as they climbed
the steep muddy track towards the hospital
towers. Groups of onlookers gathered: Turks,
and a few pale British soldiers in rags of uniform, some with an arm missing, or limping.
There were a few women too, near the Barrack
gate, more wretched-looking, if that were possible, than the men, cooking horrible lumps of
meat over poor fires.

"Good luck, ma'am," one soldier said respectfully as they passed, but on the whole there was silence all around.

They entered the gate, under the archway and into the huge square in the center of the Barrack. One side of the enormous building had been burned down, and gaunt black timbers stood out like broken bones. In the middle of the sea of mud and refuse, which, they had been told, had been a parade ground for twelve thousand men, a broken fountain stood. It began to rain again.

Miss Nightingale was waiting for them with Major Sillery, the commandant.

"We have allotted you," said the Major briskly, "one of the towers. It has a number of rooms and you will be able to be more or less private."

They trooped up the stairs at the Major's heels. Never had a more depressing sight struck their eyes, not even in Bermondsey, in the poorest homes, in the cholera epidemic. Poverty and filth in small quantities, room by room, was bad enough. But here was poverty and filth running for miles through dirty, dreary, echoing corridors (there were no patients on this side of the hospital), in the mildewed, cracked and oozing walls, and the rotten greeny-black floors. The smell, even on the uninhabited side, was awful.

They were ushered into the tower, where a dark hall had a number of doors opening from it. Each room was absolutely empty and as dirty as the one before. Each had some sort of tattered matting on the floor, and a raised dais, called a divan, running around the walls.

Major Sillery coughed. "Not very comfortable for ladies, I'm afraid." His voice, though friendly, suggested that they had been extremely foolish to come at all. "I'll see to it that bedding is brought in."

Later that evening, the five Bermondsey nuns sat on the edge of their divan in a not very cheerful row. Since the Norwood nuns had not arrived yet, their room was not crowded—not nearly as bad as the one next door, where all the nurses were squashed in.

Each had a tin basin of so-called tea in front of her and a piece of hard bread. Reverend Mother made the sign of the cross.

"Bless us, O Lord, and these thy gifts. . . ."

They were grateful for this supper, for at one time it had seemed likely that they would get nothing at all. Miss Nightingale had somehow managed to conjure up a pail of hottish water in which the tea leaves floated sadly. Someone had produced a little brown sugar to sweeten the brew, and a loaf of sour Turkish bread had somehow come from the soldiers' ration store. No arrangements had been made to make the women welcome, or even to issue them rations.

Supper over, Sister Stanislaus stood on the one piece of furniture, a backless chair, and stuffed the gaping window panes with pieces of paper. They wrapped their rugs around them and tried to warm their hands.

Miss Nightingale came in to visit them, quiet, self-possessed, as though this were what one expected in hospitals. She sat down on the chair.

"The hospital is, I am afraid, as bad as it ever was," she said quietly. "If there have been any improvements they are not apparent. They are short of everything. The men are lying without beds, without shirts. There is no special food. Even the fever and dysentery cases have to eat ration bread and meat—or else starve."

She spoke in a flat, even voice, as though she had determined that not one ounce of precious energy should be wasted on anger.

"If we could get the poor fellows clean—and fed," she said, "they would die more easily. As for curing them—there seem to be no medicines, no splints, almost no bandages."

"Tell us what to do," said Sister Gonzaga impatiently.

"For the moment—nothing."

"*Nothing?*"

"There will be delays. Most of the medical

men do not want us. We are an insult to them, a doubt cast on their efficiency. They will not allow that anything is wrong. They have assured the Government at home that nothing is wrong, so of course they have to stick to their word. But—and I want your loyalty and support in this—we are not going to do anything until we are asked."

"This will be very hard," said Reverend Mother gently, "with the men in as bad a state as you say." She meant, but did not say, "hard for *you*," for she saw that Miss Nightingale was a person who would wear herself to pieces with passion which was not allowed to show.

"This will be very hard," said Miss Nightingale, with the steely ring in her voice that they were soon to know very well. "I have plenty of money, and stores. But we are here to work *for* the doctors, not against them. I want that clearly understood."

She looked at each one in turn.

"Men will have to die," she said. "But we are here to fight for something bigger than the lives of these few. We are here to fight for the future of the nurse, and the future of the soldier. Is that understood?"

She looked at them almost angrily.

"We are entirely in your hands," said Reverend Mother gently. "I hope we shall not add to your troubles by any disloyalty."

None of them slept much that night. The army palliasses were hard, and the divan full of fleas. The wind whistled through the broken panes, blowing out the plugs of paper. They were cold, miserable, far from home and frightened. Worst of all, perhaps they were not to be used for the purpose for which they had come.

CHAPTER FIVE

The Work Begins

FATHER MICHAEL CUFFE, CATHOLIC CHAPLAIN
to the Barrack Hospital, was saying Mass in
his room. The altar was a pile of his baggage,
with an altar stone (the altar stone from the
Bermondsey convent) laid on top. His congre-
gation consisted of five nuns from Bermondsey,
quite overjoyed to have Mass on their very
first morning, their old friend from London,
Father Butt, who was at Scutari to recover

from a fever, and one or two orderlies, one of whom was serving Mass.

The room, which the two priests shared, was no cleaner or better furnished than the ones in the tower, but, thought Reverend Mother as she knelt in thanksgiving after Communion, there was so much to be thankful for.

It was strange to look back upon the last few Sundays: one in the familiar chapel in Bermondsey; one in Paris, with a French priest giving a French sermon, which always sounds so odd to English ears; one lying flat on a tossing bunk in the Mediterranean, with the splash and thump of the waves outside; one in this bare room in the Scutari Hospital. What of those ahead?

Perhaps it was just as well that she could not see them. Life would often be unbearable except that it has to be taken one day at a time.

After dinner—army rations of stringy boiled beef and sour bread—there was a general invitation from the Sellonites, who had the room upstairs, to come and look at the view.

"We have *ten* windows, fancy that," said Sister Sarah gaily to Sister Gonzaga, to whose side, as usual, she had made her way, "and nearly all of them broken. I can assure you we have our full ration of fresh air."

Sister Gonzaga did not answer with a joke. She felt depressed. Even half a day's waiting,

when there was so much to be done, was trying. She moved from window to window, looking out at the view, which was a glorious one.

On one side she looked across flat country
to the Bosphorus, and beyond the Bosphorus
lay Constantinople in a gleaming panorama,
glittering in the afternoon sun with hundreds of
mosques and minarets. Nearer, in Scutari itself, there was a view straight down a Turkish
street, with all the little shops, and their owners
sitting cross-legged outside, smoking their long
pipes. Everywhere there seemed to be packs of
wild stray dogs.

It was all so bright and picturesque that for
a moment she felt better, until from the third
window, looking down towards the main gate
of the hospital, she saw the thin ragged procession of wounded men coming up from the
jetty. Even at that distance, there was something dreadfully pathetic in their staggering
steps and bent heads. Some, obviously, were
kept going only by the thought that ahead of
them was a place where they could lie down
and die.

Tears of anger and distress started to her
eyes, but with an effort she controlled them.

On the other side of the room, Miss Nightingale and Reverend Mother were talking in a
low voice. Miss Nightingale had been pointing
out another building some half a mile away.

"That is the General Hospital," she said, "and it has also been handed over to the English. The doctors there, I believe, are not unfriendly, and in a day or two I hope to send some nurses over."

Then she lowered her voice further: "I am much struck by the look of Sister Mary Gonzaga, as well as by her behavior on the journey. Would you say that she would be a suitable person to send up there? I notice that she gets on particularly well with the nurses and the Anglican Sisters."

Reverend Mother agreed, and in a few words told of Sister Gonzaga's immense energy, sense of humor, and ability to cope cheerfully with almost any difficulties.

"She has no faults, your paragon," said Miss Nightingale with a smile.

"She has the faults of her virtues," said Reverend Mother. "She spends herself entirely and lives on her nerves. When the crisis is over, there comes a reaction. But as long as one needs her, no better person can be found."

The next few days were tedious, for they had to wait. Some of the nurses were in a state of open rebellion, for they thought it was all Miss Nightingale's fault. She, however, was working behind the scenes to win over the doctors, and in one important particular she got her own way very early. They allowed her to open an extra diet kitchen for the men who could not eat the army rations, and within forty-eight hours, with Reverend Mother and Mrs. Clark at work in it, the tower kitchen and "Reverend Mother's store" were, apart from Miss Nightingale's own office, the most efficient places in the hospital.

"This is our first victory," she said a day or two later, as she came in with a smiling face. The kitchen was only a small room, and it was crowded to overflowing with boxes and supplies. Reverend Mother was making a fragrant brew of warm wine and water in a bucket on one stove; Mrs. Clark was stirring a pail of arrowroot and milk on the other. A line of orderlies were waiting for the rations for their wards. Keeping them in order was Sergeant Tom Vickery. This was the orderly who had served Mass on Sunday, and he had promptly attached himself to Reverend Mother and turned himself into her slave. As the orderlies were Turkish and Greek as well as English, it was not always easy to explain things to them, but where Vickery's exasperated "parley-vooing" was useless, Reverend Mother seemed able always to restore order by raising an eyebrow or, in very severe cases of insubordination, shaking a finger.

Miss Nightingale inspected the kitchen and found everything as good as could be expected, but she was called out suddenly and came back with a very different look on her face.

"We are really needed," she said, "at last. There has been another battle. At least five hundred wounded are expected—in half an hour."

On that Sunday morning when they had all stood in the tower in the sunshine and looked at the view, the third great battle of the war, Inkerman, had been fought in the Crimea. They called it the "soldiers' battle," for the British lines were surprised so quickly that the men had turned out of their tents, snatched up their weapons, and fought, under any officer who could be found to lead them, or even on their own. It was a sullen struggle in fog and smoke. In the end, with the help of the French, the Russian attack had been beaten off, but the casualties had been very heavy. And news of this battle and of the great number of wounded, arrived, through some mistake, at Scutari only half an hour before the transports came in.

This was Miss Nightingale's chance to show what she and her nurses could do. There was no time for jealousy. There was work for all, and all were needed.

Sister Mary Gonzaga was not in the Barrack Hospital when the news came. The doctors at the other hospital had proved friendly, and that very morning a party of ten nurses had set out to work for them. Sister Gonzaga and Sister Anastasia, three Sellonites (Sister Sarah had managed to include herself, of course), and five nurses started out to walk, but they found that a "carriage" was waiting. At sight of it they burst into peals of laughter.

Where it had come from nobody quite knew, but it was a great gilded uncomfortable coach, more suitable for the Lord Mayor's Show than a muddy hilltop in Turkey, with two large slow horses and a large slow Turkish coach-man sitting cross-legged on the box, smoking his pipe very seriously.

The Sisters, being young and active, all said they would rather walk in spite of the rain and mud, but the nurses preferred to ride.

So it was arranged. But when it came to getting in, Sister Gonzaga and Sister Anastasia had to walk away hurriedly, for fear of not being able to control themselves. They stopped a little way off and watched, however. The sight was too good to miss.

The carriage had no door! Mrs. Lawfield, a good soul but large and somewhat given to grumbling, was determined to ride. First she put one foot up, and then she put it down and put the other up, and then she stuck altogether, halfway through the low window. At last the driver, getting impatient, gave her a shove, and in she went, landing on the cushions inside with a muffled squeak. Then her face appeared at the window and she could be heard saying: "And how I'm to get out again, I don't know."

At last the carriage with its cargo started, plodding very slowly through the mud. The walkers, with their skirts kilted out of the wet, made much better time. Once they heard distant cries, and, looking back, saw that the Turk had unharnessed his horses and led them away.

"Oh dear," said Sister Gonzaga, "perhaps we had better go back as a rescue party. What can he mean to do?"

But he was only taking them off for a drink, and presently brought them back and harnessed them up again.

Meanwhile the walkers were not only getting extremely muddy, for it had rained heavily in the night, but were being annoyed by packs of wild dogs, which came much nearer than anybody liked. However, some active work by Sister Gonzaga with her umbrella, and some words in a surprisingly unconventual voice which she confessed to having heard the farmers use in her childhood, won the day.

On the hospital doorstep they were met by a gentleman who said that he was just riding over to see Miss Nightingale, and could he do anything for them?

"Yes, please, fetch us a boat to go backwards and forwards in," said Sister Gonzaga, laughing, but looking rather ruefully at her splashed habit and sodden boots.

The General Hospital, though not so large as the Barrack, still looked much the same. There seemed to be hundreds of miles of beds with rough mattresses, and as soon as the transports began to land the first of the Inkerman wounded, there was more than enough for all the nurses to do.

Most of the men, even those who were obviously dying, walked up from the jetty, or rather crept and crawled, for there was no other means of transportation. A few were carried on stretchers, but the Turkish bearers were rough and careless. Some died on the way up, some died almost as soon as they were tipped into bed. Most were near starvation as well as suffering from wounds. They had been roughly bandaged up four days before, after the battle, and no one had looked at them since.

Before the doctors could attend to them, they had to be undressed and put to bed. At first some of them, even those barely conscious, put up a feeble resistance at the thought of ladies waiting on them.

"No ma'am, no, don't you be doing that," protested a sergeant of the 20th as Sister Gonzaga began to undress him.

"Hush," she said firmly, "this is what your mother would be doing if she were here."

He looked at her with grateful eyes, and argued no more.

"Why," she said, as she took away the battered forage cap which he still wore over his bandages, "this is the number of the Lancashire Fusiliers. I was born near Preston."

"Nay," Sergeant Parker tried to sit up but fell back with an exhausted groan, "a Lancashire lass! Beg your pardon, ma'am, but this is as good as home."

While she unwound the dirty bandages and washed his stiff wounds that had not been touched for four days, he tried to tell her about the battle.

"There weren't many of us, but we gave 'em the Minden yell—have ye ever heard it, ma'am?"

"No, no thank you," said Sister Gonzaga hastily, afraid that he might be going to demonstrate.

"Well, it's a special of the 20th, and a rare good 'un, and then we charged them Rooshians. I got this on the head first, and then this one through my wrist, but I weren't going to give in for them. But this in my side, see, that dropped me, and there weren't no more fighting for me after."

Sister Gonzaga finished washing his wounds,

took her bucket of hot water and her hand-fuls of lint on to the next bed. As she did so Sergeant Parker gave her a huge wink and said: "I'll always remember the fifth of November, ma'am."

She felt as she turned away, hiding her smiles, that he, at least, would recover.

Of the next man she could not feel so hope-ful. He had a Scots Fusilier uniform, so the orderly said who helped her to lift him. He could barely speak, though he managed to say that his name was Sergeant Gordon. She sup-pressed a shudder as she unwrapped the right hand that had been torn by the shell fragments that had also broken his ribs and wounded him badly in the body. He was very weak and in great pain, not only from his wounds, but also from the sores on his back as a result of having lain helpless on the deck of the so-called hospi-tal ship as she had rolled her way across the Black Sea.

"Ask the doctor to come to this man as soon as possible," she said to the orderly in a low voice. She was just moving on when the Ser-geant opened his eyes.

"I'd like to see my wife and the lads again," he said.

"And so you shall, I hope," she said sooth-ingly. "Here comes the doctor, and he'll see to you."

She had never worked so hard before in all her life as she did that day, but it was good work, and at the end of it her mind was full of terrible things, but also of pictures of unbelievable courage and humor. The walk through the cold evening air did them all good, although it was raining, and the thought of Reverend Mother and the others in the little tower room was like the thought of home.

Sister Gonzaga had been so busy with her own affairs all day that she was surprised to find that wounded men had been pouring into the big hospital too. The first sign of it was that the long empty corridor leading to their rooms was empty no longer. They had to pick their way between a double line of wounded men, laid, not on beds, because the supply of beds had run out, but on sacks of straw, with the drafts whistling along the dirty stone floors.

The whole mechanism of the hospital had broken down, and the place was in turmoil. The wounded men had poured in all day in a never-ending stream, many of them dying as soon as they arrived. Those less badly wounded had a frightful tale to tell, of so-called hospital ships moored in the harbor at Balaclava. It had taken two weeks to fill some of these ships— two weeks during which the firstcomers had lain on the decks without medical attention, men with wounds, cholera, amputations, dysentery, and no one to do anything for them except tip them overboard when they died. It was no wonder that even a sack of straw on a dirty floor seemed a haven of rest, and Mrs. Clark, going around with her saucepan of soup, and jollying the poor fellows along as she doled out the mugfuls, seemed like a rather solid kind of angel.

Scutari was as badly organized as Miss Nightingale had feared. The doctors had worked all day and were prepared to work all night, but they had no equipment. There was not an operating table. There was not even a screen to prevent the other patients from seeing arms and legs being taken off. Many of the beds were without blankets; the men lay on their sacks of straw, covered only with their great-coats, stiff with dirt and blood. The sanitary arrangements mostly did not work. The drains were blocked and the filth and the smell were horrible. And still the hospital ships were coming in.

And yet, when it was suppertime, the nuns were astonished to find how hungry they were, and how good the meal tasted, though the butter was rancid and the cheese was moldy, and there was very little of either. On one point Miss Nightingale was very strict—that the nurses should not be better treated than the soldiers. They were not to use the extra diet kitchen for themselves, but line up for their army rations like the men. It was in ways like this, she said, that they could prove to the authorities that women in a hospital were an advantage and not a burden.

And after all, the evening ended with a laugh. Sister de Chantal, who had been to Miss Nightingale's office, came back bursting with laughter. She had overheard poor Mrs. Lawfield, aged, dignified, and forty-two inches round the waist, making a complaint to the Lady Superintendent.

"I came out, ma'am, prepared to submit to everything, to be put upon in every way. But there are some things, ma'am, that one can't submit to. There is the caps, ma'am, that suits one face and some that suits another. And if I'd known, ma'am, about the caps, great as was my desire to come out to nurse at Scutari, I wouldn't have come, ma'am."

Miss Nightingale, starting out for her round of the wards with Mrs. Roberts, her lantern in her hand, heard the laughter that followed Sister de Chantal's story, and thought, as Sister Gonzaga had thought of Sergeant Parker, that these would be the ones to survive whatever lay ahead.

CHAPTER SIX

Sergeant Gordon

IT WAS A GOOD THING, IN THOSE DARK DAYS AT Scutari, to be a nun. The muddle and the suffering and the waste of human lives would have been too terrible without God. One could not suppose that He approved, but at least He knew about it all, and this made it easier to bear.

Soon things fell into such a steady routine that the Sisters felt they had spent half their lives in the hospitals. Sister Mary Stanislaus had

charge of A corridor. Little Sister Anastasia
was also promoted to be in charge of a corridor, so it was Sister de Chantal who now went
daily to the General Hospital with Sister Gonzaga.

The latter wrote home: "Now we are toler-
ably settled to our work though nothing here
is very settled. Miss Nightingale is very kind to
us—prefers us to all the rest. Rev. Mother is a
general favorite with all parties and is invaluable for keeping peace, rather difficult in these
parts."

Indeed Reverend Mother, after Miss Nightingale, was the most respected person in the
hospital. She did not often go into the wards,
but divided her time between Mrs. Clark's
kitchen and the store on C corridor, which was
a perfect bazaar of soups, canned meat, jam,
arrowroot, spaghetti, feather pillows, mittens,
scarves, port wine, shirts, handkerchiefs, writing paper. Here she reigned supreme, with
Vickery as Prime Minister, and many people,
from the Protestant chaplain downwards, made
excuses to drop in and talk to her.

The trouble in the hospital was not so much
shortage of goods, as the difficulty of making
the medical men accept help. Miss Nightingale
had brought a large sum of money with her,
and the *Times* newspaper had started a fund
which soon rose to thousands of pounds. Every

ship brought hundreds of bales of free gifts
from people in England. The difficulty was
partly to sort and store this great collection of
stuff, partly to make anybody use it.

Miss Nightingale was absolutely determined
that she would work only with the doctors,
not against them. As she said, she was fighting
for the future of the nurse and the future of
the soldier.

Her quiet determination paid, but it paid at
the cost of great suffering. Some of her nurses
were furious with her because even when men
were starving to death, she would not give
them a teaspoonful of arrowroot without a
doctor's orders, and some of the doctors refused to give these orders. This was the cause
of much bitterness. Good nurses had to watch
their patients die, and they could not forgive
Miss Nightingale.

But she knew what she was doing. As the
situation worsened, and the sick and wounded
continued to pour into the ill-provided Barrack
Hospital (at one moment in this terrible winter
there were 12,000 sick in the hospitals, and
only 11,000 men still on their feet in the army
before Sevastopol), the doctors' pride and jealousy broke down to a certain extent, and she
was allowed to do what she could. Victory did
not come all at once, but it came in the end.

But there were worse days ahead. Sister

Gonzaga had not spent more than a week at the General Hospital when one evening, on the way home, she and Sister de Chantal were caught in a torrent of rain. There was a strange drumming wind up the Bosphorus, and their umbrellas were useless as shelter.

They went into the diet kitchen to dry themselves a little by the fire, for their habits were soaked.

"If you'll excuse me, Sister," said Tom Vickery severely, as though they were children and he their nurse, "you ought to change them wet things. I'll hang them in the big kitchen downstairs—it's hotter than this one—and they'll be dry by morning."

There was nothing to do but spend the evening in bed while the wet habits and boots were being dried. Wrapped in their rugs, they sat up in bed and, sharing the single candle between them, darned the community's spare stockings and listened to the wind and rain lashing the windows. It was going to be a wild night. They were glad at least that the windows had been mended—by order of Miss Nightingale, for no one else would have bothered.

Their evening prayers over, the Sisters gathered around the candle in a nightly routine which by now they were so accustomed to that it was neither funny nor disgusting. They took off their habits and spent an hour or more picking off the lice. The whole hospital was verminous, so that if one started to write a letter in the wards, the paper was soon crawling with the creatures.

The storm was so noisy that they got little sleep. Sister Gonzaga woke several times and listened to the howl of the wind, and wondered whether the Sellonites, in their ten-windowed apartment upstairs, were being blown out of bed.

That storm blew the poor English army on the heights above Sevastopol almost into the sea. It wrecked a great number of ships, including one that was full of winter clothing, and it was the beginning of the Crimean winter.

Balaclava, the harbor, was separated from the camp by eight miles of road, and the eight miles turned into a bog. The men had to cross that awful eight miles to get everything, even fodder for the horses, who were soon so hungry that they had not strength to fetch up their own food, let alone carry the men's as well. By the waterside were stacked the neatly numbered pieces of prefabricated wooden huts, and there was no way of carrying them up to the bare hillside where men were dying of cold and frostbite.

To read the whole story now is almost unbearable, and we wonder how anyone could have lived and worked through it and not been driven mad, but luckily human beings never see things as a whole. They see their own little bit of the picture, and the busier they are, the smaller does that little bit become, for they have no time to look outside it.

So to Sister Gonzaga, working day by day in the General Hospital, there was much that was hopeful, and even amusing, as she went her rounds day by day.

The wounded men nearly always managed to be cheerful. One day, she was dressing a horribly gangrened leg, and the man insisted on sitting up in bed and drawing a plan of the battle of Inkerman on it to show what he had been doing on that fateful November 5th.

"Och, Sister dear, you're not attending," he said sadly.

"I was trying not to hurt you too much."

"Sure, never mind that. Now, see here. There's the city of Sevastopol, and there's the harbor, with seven ships sunk across it. Do you see now?"

"I understand about the seven ships," she said, "but you must let me go now. I'll promise to come for the rest of my lesson tomorrow."

She paused by the bed of her cheerful Lancashire friend with a pang of dismay. The bed was empty. But she was reassured by a voice from the middle of the room, and saw with pleasure that Sergeant Parker was up, pale and gaunt, but sitting by the stove in his blue hospital dressing gown.

He stood up to greet her. "I'm past nursing, Sister, and looking after the others now."

"I've brought you a clean shirt," she said, taking one from the pile that the orderly was carrying for her.

"This has been a right good day," he said enthusiastically. "A clean shirt, and a newspaper from home. See here, Sister, all this bit about the battle of the Alma. He's got it all right too. Must have been right there himself, the chap as wrote this."

Obviously, from the circle around him, he had been reading aloud "the bit about the battle." And all up and down the ward, badly wounded men were trying to sit up in their beds, and their faces had brightened with interest.

"Ay," they said, "it were just so. . . . That was it, I was in that charge. . . . Now that bit's wrong, and I'll tell you why."

A newspaper was evidently the best tonic that they could hope for, but the second best was the pile of clean shirts, issued from Miss Nightingale's store, that Sister Gonzaga distributed.

"Where's your old one?" she said to one man.

"The bugs fair eat it to pieces," he said sadly.

"It's under his mattress," said his neighbor, indignantly, not approving of this attempt to tell lies to "the lady."

The orderly bent down to investigate and whipped out a filthy rag.

"Why did you hide it? I'm going to send it to the laundry."

"I'd rather have my dirt than some other chap's," he answered sullenly. "We've had things from the laundry before, and they came back worse than they went."

"This time it will be quite different. Miss Nightingale has got a real laundry now—haven't you heard? The engineers have put in boilers for her, and things really get clean."

He handed over the old shirt willingly enough now, and as she gave him a new one, saying, "Can you put it on yourself, or will I ask someone to help you?" he snatched her hand and gave it a quick rough kiss. She pulled back in astonishment and he looked acutely embarrassed, but muttered, almost angrily, "We never knew there was such angels as you nurses."

Sergeant Parker handed on the paper to another reader and came up to the Sister.

"Charlie's been asking for you," he said.

"Sergeant Gordon?"

"Yes. I'm afraid he's not going to last long, ma'am. You know he seemed to be better since they took his hand off, and he was reading the Bible you gave him, quite comfortable, last night, but he's very low this morning."

She went over to Sergeant Gordon's bed.

"Can I get you anything, Sergeant?"

"Nothing now, ma'am, thank you. You've done everything for me my own mother could have done. But when I'm gone, if you'd be so kind, could you write a bit of a letter about me to my wife. And the two bairns. They'll want to know about their dad."

Death was all around, and no one went about making falsely cheerful promises. Sister Gonzaga took out her notebook and sat on the floor.

"Will you tell me the address?" she said.

"'Ere, sit on this," hoarsely whispered Sergeant Parker, thrusting his rolled-up blanket towards her. A moment later he was limping rapidly down the ward, bellowing to someone, in something very like his old parade-ground voice: "Now then, 'ush up there. None of them words. Can't you see t'lady's 'ere?"

It was no place to be dying, this long, echoing, noisy, comfortless room, with the orderlies pushing between the rows of beds, and a doctor doing his rounds in the distance, and the convalescents smoking and arguing around the fire.

Sister Gonzaga had to bend over to catch the man's weak voice.

"Shall I get the chaplain for you?" she said.

"No, thank you, I'm a Presbyterian myself and not fond of parsons. I have the Testament you brought me, and I've read a bit in that. There's a great deal of comfort in the psalms."

"What shall I tell your wife?"

"Just tell her that God wished it, and it had to be, and that I don't mind going, though I'd have liked fine to see her and the boys again."

That evening Sister Gonzaga came into the tower very quietly. She found the room only half its usual size, for Reverend Mother was rigging up a white calico curtain to divide it down the center. The Norwood nuns, now that there was enough work for all, had come across from Constantinople, and it seemed better to try to give each little community a minimum of privacy so that they could keep to their own hours and their own ways of ordering their lives.

"How useful it is to have charge of the stores," Reverend Mother was saying from her position on the old chair, hammering in nails. "I have been guilty of what Vickery calls 'a prig.' I'm learning a great deal of army slang. Why, Sister, you look very low."

"One of my patients died this afternoon, and I must write to his wife."

After tea, when the others had gone back to their wards for the last patrol, she sat down on the edge of the divan and arranged her writing paper and inkpot on the old chair—still the only table they had. She dipped her pen and began:

"Dear Mrs. Gordon,

I promised to write and tell you all I could about your husband. You have already heard that he was very much wounded—I believe by a shell. At first he seemed to suffer much from the wound in his body, but then he seemed to rally and we were in hopes that he would recover, but God pleased to ordain otherwise. . . ."

She dropped her pen and thought of the poor widow with her two little boys to educate, and of the many, many others like her. But it was no good thinking sad thoughts when there was work to be done. She wrote on carefully, remembering that this would be the only news the poor woman would ever have, and writing every detail she could think of—about the Testament, and Sergeant Parker's rough kindness, and what had happened to his watch and money.

"It is difficult for me to try to comfort you, for I know it must indeed be a heavy blow to you. I can but advise you to think often that God is a loving Father, and only afflicts in mercy, and that what is so great a grief to you may be a greater joy to your husband. . . ."

Such words were well-meaning, but did they really *say* anything? Could they bring any comfort to a poor woman looking eagerly for the postman every day? Only prayer could bridge that unbridgeable gap. She wrote on, her heart full of feeling that could not express itself on paper.

". . . I am sure you loved him too much to wish to bring him back from Heaven. I can only promise my prayers for him and for you and for your children. May God bless and comfort you all.

I am, my dear Mrs. Gordon,
Yours faithfully in Christ,
Sister Mary Gonzaga."

CHAPTER SEVEN

A Strange Christmas

EVERY NIGHT MISS NIGHTINGALE, WITH THE lamp in her hand and Mrs. Roberts to keep her company, walked around the four miles of beds in the Barrack Hospital. It was an eerie errand of mercy, miles of darkness and the restless tossing and delirious cries of sick men. There was no one else on duty in the wards at that time of night except the orderlies, who usually slept soundly enough, and she saved many a man's life by sending for the doctor at a crucial moment, and she helped many a man to die by sitting beside him.

The men adored her. "She would speak to one, and nod and smile to as many more," one of them said. "But she could not do it all, you know. We lay there by hundreds; but we could kiss her shadow as it fell and lay our heads on the pillow again content."

One night, on this long walk, she saw a light still burning in Reverend Mother's store, and went in, to find Mother Mary Clare still busy over some accounts that had to be finished before the next day's business began.

"Come to my room when you have finished," she said, "and Mrs. Roberts shall make us a cup of tea. We are both tired and it will do us good."

Over their mugs of tea they talked of the work.

"December fourteenth," said Miss Nightingale, looking down at a half-finished letter lying in the clutter of papers on her desk. "We have been here six weeks, Reverend Mother, and I believe we are making headway at last. I am sending a list of what we have done to the Secretary of State for War. I hope he will be impressed. It is not only that we are actually nursing, but there is the laundry, and the poor soldiers' wives being looked after, and, what I think the most important, the whole of that burnt-out wing of the hospital put into repair again. Eight hundred extra beds which would not be there at all but for yours truly gingering up the authorities!"

"And all the cleaning of the wards," said Reverend Mother.

"Yes. Two hundred scrubbing brushes I have issued. That has made a difference. And then, of course, your kitchen. If any of us is to get a reward in heaven for saving lives, you and Mrs. Clark will have to line up first, Reverend Mother."

Then she sighed. "Three of my nurses must go home, I'm afraid."

"I am sorry to hear it."

"So am I. Two of the old things got drunk, I'm afraid. No great harm done, and when you think what they have been through, and what these hospital nurses are usually like, it's no great wonder. But we cannot have it *here*. We must be above reproach. They'll go on the mailboat next week. And then that unfortunate Sellonite, Sister Elizabeth. Foolish woman, writing letters home without checking her facts."

"That put you in a very unhappy position," said Reverend Mother.

"Yes, indeed. Here am I trying to convince the authorities that we are their loyal band of helpers, and one of my own nurses attacks the army, the hospital, and everything else in a public letter. So she must go—but she's a good nurse, and I'm very sorry about it. Oh, Reverend Mother, if I had forty Bermondsey nuns to work for me I should be a happy woman. However, we must give thanks for what we have managed to do already, and not grumble."

Reverend Mother said good night and left her. As she shut the door she saw Miss Nightingale, still sitting at her little square table, and once more writing, writing, writing.

Next day a storm broke in the "Female Nursing Establishment." Miss Nightingale found out, quite casually, that a further party of forty nuns, ladies and nurses was coming from England to join her. No one had asked her permission, although she had been ¹promised that no more would come unless she sent for them and until she thought that the doctors would accept more. What was worse, fifteen of them were Irish Sisters of Mercy. If she turned them back, there would be a revolution in Ireland, as she said. If she accepted them, there would be a storm of protest and abuse from those who thought that the ten Roman Catholics already on the nursing strength were the result of a Jesuit plot.

Reverend Mother was called in to use all her

tact and kindness to make peace. She did not relish her job. Much as she liked and admired Miss Nightingale, she knew her for a woman of ruthless single-mindedness, not easily swayed. And she knew, moreover, the superior of the Irish nuns, Reverend Mother Bridgeman from Kinsale, another woman of great decision and strength of character, who could see little good in anyone not a Catholic.

So it was not with pleasure that she looked forward to the moment when Reverend Mother Bridgeman, who had been staying at the convent in Constantinople, came across the water with a companion by caique for a high-level conference with the Lady Superintendent.

They were welcomed first by Reverend Mother and taken to the nuns' room. Everyone else was out at the time, working, but the sight of the small room with its scanty curtain, its ten makeshift beds, horrified the two Irish nuns.

"But how can they make you live here?" Reverend Mother Bridgeman was appalled. "One room for ten of you. It's monstrous! How dare they? You should have had a suite of rooms at least."

Reverend Mother tried, without any success, to point out that it was not the result of some plot by the Protestants.

"Miss Nightingale was allowed only these few rooms for forty of us. We are no worse off than the others. But you see why Miss Nightingale cannot take any more nuns here. There just is no accommodation."

It did not work. Nor did dinner with Miss Nightingale have a softening effect. Neither of these strong characters was at all impressed by the other—not favorably at least. They sat bolt upright and surveyed each other over the plates. Rations were poor at the time, and the only fare offered was some cold potatoes, a little butter on a saucer obviously left over from breakfast, and with the marks of a dirty knife on it, sour bread and moldy cheese.

Miss Nightingale, knowing that she would have to compromise somehow, at last made an offer in a cold voice.

"I propose, then, that I should take five of your nuns, Reverend Mother, in place of the Norwood nuns. They are not used to this work, and have already asked to be relieved when it is convenient. It will have to be sooner rather than later, that's all."

She was very angry, and she was still angry when she interviewed the superior of the Norwood nuns, who burst into tears when she and her companions were summarily dismissed and told to catch the next day's boat.

"I cannot help it," said Miss Nightingale in her iciest voice. "We have somehow got to make room for these Irish women. You had already stated that the work was too much for you."

"Yes, but we hadn't expected to be sent away—on Christmas Eve."

"I'm sorry, Sister, but there is no other way."

The nuns would not be comforted, although later, when they realized the position she had been cornered in, they held no grudge against Miss Nightingale. She, in turn, quickly recovered from her anger, and set about writing nice letters home, thanking the Norwood nuns for their loyalty and co-operation. She had quite recovered her sense of humor when the Catholic chaplain burst in upon her later in the afternoon, brandishing the cudgels in defense of the Norwood nuns.

In short, the days just before Christmas were not marked by any particular peace or good will, and Reverend Mother, who always seemed to be the buffer state, was glad to escape to the kitchen or the store. There was something entirely satisfactory about the accounts she kept, for each item was doing real good to someone.

To take her mind off the trials and troubles of hospital life, she added up the day's output from the kitchen.

Beef tea	25 gallons
Chicken broth	15 gallons
Arrowroot	40 gallons
Sago	15 gallons
Barley water	240 quarts
Rice pudding	275 portions
Wine	21 bottles

She wished, as she went to bed, that human beings could use all the energy they wasted in quarreling with one another, in brewing more and more gallons of beef tea and arrowroot. For, impressive though the list sounded, it was not so impressive when you remembered that there were more than 3000 men in the hospital. . . .

Perhaps because she was the eldest, Reverend Mother was the lightest sleeper and could be relied on to wake every morning at six precisely, even when everything outside was black dark, and while the younger nuns still slept the sleep of exhaustion.

So it was arranged that she should be vigilatrix and wake the others. This morning she opened her eyes in the dark, and her usual sixth sense told her that if she looked at her watch it would say six o'clock. Shivering a little, she lit the candle, then knelt down to say a brief prayer before waking the others. Prayers got briefer and briefer these days, and often had to be something like the old Cavalier's prayer before a battle:

"Lord, I shall be very busy this day. If I forget Thee, do not Thou forget me."

She put on her habit, and then took the jug and went quietly out to fetch water for the others. She often saved them trouble like this, excusing herself by saying that as she did not work in the wards, she was much less tired than they. Even five minutes extra sleep might be of service to them, she thought, her children who wore themselves out so cheerfully in the service of the sick, and still had enough bounce left in them at the end of the long day to smile and make a joke.

The early morning silence was broken as they dressed by the light of the single candle. They smiled at one another and whispered under their breath, "Happy Christmas."

And as they tiptoed in single file between the long rows of beds, on the way to Father Cuffe's room, heads were raised to greet them.

"Merry Christmas! . . . Happy Christmas, Sister!"

This was always the quietest hour of the twenty-four. The worst of the night was over, and the business of the vast hospital had not begun. Exhausted men who had been unable to sleep, and feared to die in the dark, were cheered by the coming of the dawn and lay

quietly. . . . Tonight was a long way off.
Some did not wake. Twenty a night, on an
average, did not wake, and a kindly comrade
would pull the blanket decently over their
heads until the orderlies came to carry the
bodies away.

Half an hour later, after Mass, the nuns filed
back to the tower, and now the smell of
woodsmoke was spreading through the wards as
the orderlies lit fires to make the men's tea.

In the convent at home it had been the cus-
tom to have a spiritual book read at mealtimes.
Here they managed to keep up the habit.
Reverend Mother read to them while they
breakfasted, and, as she did not have to be at
work quite so early as the others, she ate her
own breakfast afterwards and did the washing-
up before she went to her kitchen. This morning, after the black tea and the bread and
butter had been handed around, she opened her
Bible and said: "I will read to you the Christmas story."

The Sisters drank from the tin basins which
were the only utensils they had, and which
served for teacups, ration plates, sometimes
even washbasins. They chewed at the hard
bread with healthy appetites which never were
quite satisfied on the poor rations. Sometimes
these things seemed trying beyond anything,
but not today.

"And she brought forth her first-born son, and wrapped him in swaddling clothes, and laid him in a manger, because there was no room for them in the inn."

Christmas is always Christmas, even at Scutari, and they put on their shawls and prepared to go off to work in great gaiety and good will. Perhaps by tonight there would be letters from home.

Sister Anastasia set off for her ward, calling next door for the nurse who was her companion. Sister Stanislaus did the same. Reverend Mother picked up the dishes. Out in the hall everyone was stirring, and you could hear them greeting each other with "Happy Christmas."

Sister Gonzaga said: "Let us go and wish Miss Nightingale a happy Christmas before we go."

"Come in!" She was (as she always was, at any hour of the day or night, apparently, except when she was actually in the wards) sitting at her table, a cup of cold tea on one side of her and a pile of papers on the other. The bed was covered with piles of papers too, and there were more on the floor.

"Thank you, my dears," she said in answer to their greeting. "But oh, dear," she shook her head, "Christmas would have more of a chance if we could boil a few stupid people with the pudding."

On the table beside her was a newspaper clipping.

"Here we are," she said, "up to our necks in blood, and all they can do at home is argue, argue, argue. Catholic and Protestant, Protestant and Catholic. All on tenterhooks in case the others should get ahead of them. I don't know which is the worst. First I have your reverend chaplain in here telling me that I'm like Herod driving the Blessed Virgin across the desert."

"He was very distressed," said Sister Gonzaga. "You must forgive him a little warmth." Then she caught Miss Nightingale's eye and they both laughed. "He's Irish," she said.

"I forgive him," said Miss Nightingale. "I can forgive anybody who makes me laugh, and that was one of the happiest moments I've had for a long time. But look at this. When it's not the Roman Catholic Storm, then it's the Protestant Howl."

She pushed over the article. It was obviously written by a very angry Protestant indeed, who must have heard somehow of Miss Nightingale's friendship with the nuns. Sister Gonzaga read it aloud, at first puzzled, then amused, and laughed outright when she got to the end and the writer's cry of alarm about "Catholic nuns transferring their allegiance from the Pope to a Protestant lady."

She dropped a sweeping curtsy, still laughing.

"Oh, Your Holiness," she said.

Miss Nightingale touched her on the shoulder with the quill of her pen.

"Rise, Cardinal Gonzaga," she said in a sepulchral voice. "I award thee the Red Hat for meritorious services. I don't suppose," she added in her ordinary voice, "that that's exactly how it's done."

Mrs. Bracebridge had come in and was looking very shocked.

"I don't think, Flo dear," she said, "that you should joke about these things."

But "Your Holiness" and "the Cardinal" they remained from that minute, and Miss Nightingale, who liked to shock people if she thought they needed it, took an impish delight in calling for her "Cardinal" in public.

Meanwhile, Sister Anastasia had gone up to her long ward on the top floor of the building. She walked around the beds behind the doctor, holding his inkstand for him, while he looked at the cases and then scribbled notes about the extra diets and dressings required. These notes were tiresome things, but no one could move an inch without them. No man could have anything issued from the stores, not a handkerchief or a cool drink, unless the doctor had signed an order. And even though the stores were her own and not the Government's, Miss Nightingale would not allow the rules to be broken. She never wavered from the plan she had laid down for herself, to win the confidence of the authorities and work with them, not against them.

The list grew—arrowroot for this man, soup for that one, a little wine and water to be given to the third at half-hourly intervals; clean shirts for these who had just come in; an air bed for that poor fellow who had spent ten days in the hold of a transport steamer, lying on the bare boards, and had worn his shoulder-blades into great sores.

So it went on. These men were lucky, for this doctor believed in the nurses, and was grateful for whatever Miss Nightingale could do. There were still some wards in which the nurses were not allowed to set foot, but had to rely on the more or less tender mercies of the orderlies, who were usually either those too old and feeble to fight, or those who preferred the comparative safety of the hospital to the front line. One of these, smoking his pipe beside the fire, was once heard to answer to a sick man calling for help: "You can wait a little, chummy; I lay a whole night once, and devil a one to wait on me; don't be too tender." And he went on calmly smoking his pipe.

But Sister Anastasia's was a good ward, and

it was, too, a ward for the wounded, who always managed to keep up some sort of cheerfulness. It was the fever wards which were so silent and depressing, where the men simply turned their faces to the wall and died, without any will to live.

The list was only half done when Mr. Osborne, one of the Protestant chaplains, came in. He smiled at Sister Anastasia, and spoke to the doctor. Then he stood in the middle of the room and wished them all a merry Christmas. He had a strong voice, and the wounded men, even in distant corners, stirred in their beds and looked towards him.

"Miss Nightingale," he said, "has had a message from Her Majesty, which she thinks you would like to hear."

There was dead silence while he read out the letter.

"'I wish Miss Nightingale and the ladies would tell these poor noble wounded and sick men that *no one* takes a warmer interest or feels more for their suffering, or admires their courage and heroism *more* than their Queen. Day and night she thinks of her beloved troops. So does the Prince!'"

The man beside Sister Anastasia caught his breath. He was only a boy, pale and thin as a skeleton.

"She thinks of us," he said wonderingly,

while the easy tears started to his eyes. "She's a Queen that is very fond of her soldiers."

"I only wish I could go and fight for her again," growled a voice from another bed.

A one-armed sergeant sitting by the fire stood up. In a voice that still had some faint echo of the barrack square he said:

"Come on, boys. Three cheers for the great Queen, God bless her. Hip, hip. . . ."

And from every corner of the long ward came the feeble hoarse hurrahs of men almost too ill to speak at all. The chaplain hastily turned his head aside and busied himself nailing up the paper on the wall beside the door.

The round over, Sister Anastasia hurried away down the stairs to Reverend Mother's storeroom with her list, while an orderly took the other half of it to the kitchen. Everything that was wanted was easily found, except the air bed.

"Now I'm afraid those are in the other store, Sister."

"Oh *no*, Reverend Mother!"

"Yes, but they're just at the foot of the ladder. It isn't far to go. Or shall I go for you?" She knew what was bothering Sister Anastasia.

"Certainly not," said the little Sister, gathering up her dignity. She hurried away and

Reverend Mother called after her: "Try holy water, Sister!"

There were three storerooms in the hospital. Reverend Mother's was comparatively dry, and, owing to her efforts, was in beautiful order. But no one had time to sort out all the stuff that was constantly pouring in, much of it in small, assorted, ill-tied parcels from kind and muddly people at home who wanted to help and really did not know what to do. All lent a hand at the sorting when they had time, but that was not often, and the rats ran riot among the bales. In the main guard store the water seeped in from outside, and things rotted before they could be used.

The storeroom to which Sister Anastasia had to go, candle in hand, was reached by a trap-door in the floor.

She unlocked the padlock with the key Reverend Mother had given her, lifted the trap cautiously. At once she heard the familiar noise. Squeaking at the light, the great rats fled in all directions. She could hear them twittering like horrible birds, and scuttering among the bales.

She sat down on the top of the ladder and untied her boots. She set the candle on the floor where it would give most light. Then she peered down and thought she could see green eyes glowering at her from all around. She spotted the parcel she was aiming for. Then she picked up the boots, threw them one after the other as hard as she could, dashed down the ladder, saying "Shoo, shoo, shoo!" to scare off any lurkers, snatched the parcel, retrieved the boots, and was up the ladder, puffing a little, before any self-respecting rat could come to its senses.

She took her prize back to Reverend Mother. "I think I broke the record this time," she said. . . .

On the broken-backed chair was propped a little picture of the Crib, surrounded by a few twigs of evergreen that Sister de Chantal had picked on the way back from the General Hospital. It was nearly midnight. Another Christmas was nearly over.

Very softly, so as not to disturb the sick men whose beds were close by, or the nurses snoring next door, the five nuns sang in voices hardly above a whisper.

After all, on December 25th it doesn't much matter where you are.

"Adeste fideles, laeti triumphantes,
  Venite, venite in Bethlehem."

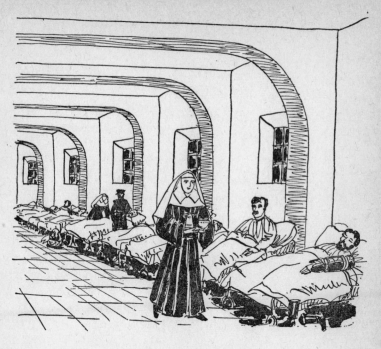

CHAPTER EIGHT

The Terrible Winter

SISTER STANISLAUS STOOD IN THE LONG QUEUE
waiting to speak to Miss Nightingale at her
desk. There was always a queue, for of all the
people in authority at the hospital, she was the
only one, in this terrible time, who seemed
to know what to do. Just the sight of her gave
people confidence. She sat at her table, pale and
composed, never raising her voice, in a black
frock with a white collar and cuffs which were

always neat and clean, and everyone came to her.

It was January now, a bitter cold January. In December it had seemed that things could not get worse, but they were worse now, and showed no signs of getting better.

Certain things had improved, largely owing to Miss Nightingale. There were beds of a kind for all the men, the floors were cleaner, the windows were mended. No one now starved to death in a hospital bed because he could not eat half-raw beef and hard bread.

But the flood of men coming in never stopped. The ships came thick and fast from Balaclava, with their helpless cargoes, and the men's stories of the dying army were terrible.

These were not wounded men. Fighting had almost stopped, for all the armies were in the same condition. These were sick men—frost-bitten, starved, suffering from dysentery and fevers. Then scurvy broke out. On January 2nd 1200 sick men were landed at Scutari at the same time, nearly all of them ill with scurvy. And yet it turned out afterwards that there were twenty thousand rations of limejuice in the stores—but no one had filled in the right forms!

There are no villains in this story. An army died of sheer muddle and inefficiency, while everyone was doing his stupid best and not getting anywhere. At Scutari only one person seemed to know what she was doing. The long queue moved up the passage, each one confident that she would solve his problem.

It was a nurse who wanted advice about a difficult treatment. Miss Nightingale gave it and took down the number of the man's bed, promising to visit him later in the day.

It was an orderly sergeant with a tale about Turkish workmen who would not understand what was required of them. Miss Nightingale promised to speak to the interpreter.

It was a message from Doctor McGrigor, one of Miss Nightingale's best friends in the hospital. A man had to have a very serious operation in half an hour's time, and could she spare the time to come and see him through it. "They always stand it better when you are there, ma'am." Miss Nightingale would be there.

It was a convalescent captain who wanted her advice about sending money home for his men. It was the *Times* almoner, entrusted with the fund money, who wanted to talk about stores. It was a Greek merchant from Constantinople, explaining in French that he had obtained the two thousand flannel shirts she had ordered. It was an invalided sergeant with only one leg, who was sailing home that afternoon and wanted the privilege of saying good-by personally. Miss Nightingale dealt with each of them as though he were the only person in the world with a problem and she had all day to give to him.

Sister Stanislaus wished the queue would move a little quicker. She felt very tired, and her head ached. Perhaps she ought to ask Reverend Mother's permission to go for half an hour's walk in the fresh cold air. But in that half hour one of her men might die, with no one beside him. No, she was all right really. She found herself leaning against the wall and stood up straight with an effort.

There were only three ahead of her now. One of the new nurses was speaking to Miss Nightingale, trying hard to control her tears. She had had word from the General Hospital that her husband, whom she had not seen since he left England with his regiment, had come in there as a patient. Might she, could she, change places with one of the nurses there so that she would be near him?

Miss Nightingale scolded her for having signed up as a nurse under false pretenses. No soldiers' wives had been taken, and the woman must have told lies to join the party. It would have been cruelty, though, not to have allowed what she asked, so she was sent off with the necessary permission.

Then it was Sister Margaret Goodman, one of the Sellonites.

"Miss Nightingale, it is too absurd. I have fifty men on an arrowroot diet, and exactly three teaspoons to feed them with."

"Have you complained to the orderly officer?"

"Yes. He said the usual thing." She recited the words they had all heard before. "'Every soldier has a spoon, knife and fork in his knapsack.' I wasn't very civil, I'm afraid. I said, 'Well, you tell me where the knapsacks are.' And he said, 'Not in my charge,' and went off in a huff. I was so vexed. Some of these poor men have never seen their knapsacks since they landed in the Crimea, because they were told to leave them behind on the ships."

Behind Sister Stanislaus was a doctor. He leaned forward to say, "My dear Sister, never vex yourself over army red tape. It never hurts them, but it can hurt you. When I was in the West Indies I was doing such a lot of office work for the regiment that I thought I'd try to claim expenses. So as a trial shot, I claimed half a crown for quill pens."

"You did not get it," said Miss Nightingale with a smile.

"Ah, there you're wrong. I got it all right, but first I spent three pounds in postage backwards and forwards explaining why I ought to have it!"

"All right, Sister Goodman," said Miss Nightingale. "We'll do this in the proper way. Find your doctor, ask him to write out a requisition for fifty spoons, and take it to the purveyor. He'll write 'None in Store' across it, and then you can bring it back to me and I'll see about it. Don't worry—your men will have their spoons by the time you want to give them their supper."

Then it was Sister Anastasia's turn, but while she was asking about extra beds in her ward, Miss Nightingale's head in front of her seemed to swell and shrink in an alarming manner, and went all wavy at the edges.

"I really am rather tired," she thought. "I had better get permission to go outdoors for a little while."

But she forgot to think about herself, for as she left she could not help hearing the doctor who had been standing behind her. He stepped up to Miss Nightingale, perfectly serious now, and said in a low voice:

"We have Asiatic cholera in the wards now. The first two cases this afternoon. I am afraid it will spread very quickly."

It did. Sister Stanislaus had no sooner got back to her own corridor than one of the men called her to look at his friend in the bed next to him. The Sister bent over him. There was no doubt what was wrong. He had come in with dysentery and had apparently been on the mend. Now, all of a sudden, he had collapsed and lay like a corpse, his skin yellow and pinched and shriveled like an old dry apple left too long in a loft. The breath that came shallowly from his half-open mouth was icy cold on her hand. She felt his feet, and they too were as cold as a stone. She sent an orderly right away for the doctor, but the man was dead before he came.

That was the beginning of the cholera epidemic. Soon it was safer even to stay and freeze on the Crimean hillside than be sent down to the hospital, for, while men were being cured of scurvy or frostbite, they caught cholera and died. They were buried at the rate of fifty a day, and still the beds were filled as fast as they were emptied.

The Barrack Hospital was a great death-house. Death seemed to be everywhere, and the men lost all hope of recovery. The long corridors were silent. The men covered their heads with their blankets and seemed to have lost the will to get better. Doctors and nurses began to sicken too. There were four thousand people in the great hospital, and it almost seemed as if they were all doomed.

And yet, though the picture was so dark,

each person living through the days and nights saw patches of light. There were still humor, and courage, and kindness.

The General Hospital nurses came off very much the best. They had their twice-daily walk to keep them healthy and the gymnastics of other people getting in and out of the "carriage" to keep them amused. Besides, there was not the same feeling of death in the air of the General. It had been built for a hospital and the drainage system was adequate. There was something so wrong with the drainage system of the Barrack that you could smell it outside the walls.

The day after the cholera outbreak, the two Bermondsey Sisters walked home as usual. They had been talking of the nurse who had changed places, and of what a wonderful tonic it would be to a sick man to see his wife come into the ward.

They came in smiling over the astonishment of a polite officer who had stepped forward to hand the ladies out of the "carriage" and found no door. It was a good thing to have an amusing story to tell at teatime, Sister Gonzaga felt. She tried to keep up the spirits of the others, for both Sister Anastasia and Sister Stanislaus looked wretchedly ill. At the moment their courage was all that kept them going. And Reverend Mother was worried by the constant demands on her to keep the peace in the "Female Nursing Establishment."

They were more comfortable in their little room, for Reverend Mother Bridgeman had refused to let her five nuns come to the hospital without her, and Miss Nightingale had refused in no uncertain terms to have them *with* her. So the Norwood nuns had gone and no one had yet come in their place. The Irish nuns still stayed over the Bosphorus with the Sisters of Charity, and relations between them and Miss Nightingale were icy cold. The Bermondsey nuns, in spite of Mother Mary Clare's efforts, came in for some of this coolness too. The Irish group regarded the Bermondsey nuns as Miss Nightingale's pets and slaves. They wrote to the Bishop about it. They thought it scandalous that the nuns should be so friendly with "a heretic." And they did not think the "Cardinal" joke was at all funny.

Bishop Grant was a kind, but a very narrow-minded, man. He loved his Bermondsey nuns dearly, but he wondered whether they had become over-enthusiastic and forgotten that they were nuns as well as nurses. He wrote anxious, fatherly letters asking for explanation of their conduct. The feeling that their own Bishop did not altogether trust them did not make the Bermondsey nuns' lives any easier.

That evening Reverend Mother handed Sister

Gonzaga a letter she had had from the Bishop. He was in Rome, but he had heard about her letter to Mrs. Gordon, which by a curious chance had been published in the *Times*. And he rebuked her for saying that a non-Catholic might go to heaven!

Sister Gonzaga's first feeling was one of anger and dismay, and Reverend Mother, seeing that she was ready to burst out with words she would be sorry for afterwards, forbade her to speak of it that night until she had slept.

Convent discipline worked to prevent the words from being spoken, but would not prevent Sister Gonzaga from lying sleepless in bed, furiously miserable. How could they, at home, understand conditions here? How could they understand that, in the presence of constant and awful death and suffering, differences simply melted away, and people became brothers? It was as natural a gesture for her to find a Protestant Bible for Sergeant Gordon as it was for Mr. Osborne to come and tell them when he had found a sick Catholic in need of help.

Sister Gonzaga might have felt better if she could have heard what an important Catholic priest (afterwards he was Cardinal Manning) had said about her letter: "A few more things like this will do us more good than all the books of controversy."

Or if she could have read a comment on herself and her Sisters in one of Miss Nightingale's letters: "They are the truest Christians I ever met with, invaluable in their work, devoted, heart and hand, to serve God and Mankind—not to intrigue for their church."

But perhaps neither of these would have helped. After all, Bishop Grant was her own Bishop. He had always been so kind—surely he must be wrong over this!

Suddenly she seemed to hear exactly what Reverend Mother wanted to say to her, in that kind, wise voice of hers. The words sounded so clear that she wondered whether perhaps Reverend Mother was awake too, and praying for her, and the words really were coming across the silence by some mysterious power. "My dear little child," Reverend Mother would say (she called them that when she wanted especially to show her love), "never mind who is right and who is wrong. That does not concern us. Let us try not to be disobedient to our superiors, even in thought, because that is always wrong."

So Sister Gonzaga won the battle against herself, and said her prayers, and felt so much lighter in heart the next day that she was particularly gay and at her most amusing. And she was able to speak very sensibly about the Bishop's letter to Reverend Mother, and say

that she thought she could write a letter of
explanation which would show that she had no
intentions of doing wrong and hoped that no
harm had been caused.

They were very busy at the General that
day and far into the evening—another ship had
come in—so that the carriage went without
them, and it was raining so hard that it was
really not fit weather to walk. Sister Gonzaga
was not officially the senior nurse, but the
others always looked up to her, and when she
said that she thought they ought not to wade
through the mud and wet across that lonely bit
of country so late in the evening, the others
agreed with her. There were only Sister de
Chantal and Sister Sarah, the little Sellonite,
and the nurse whose husband was ill. It was
partly because of her that Sister Gonzaga made
up her mind. Hospital rules would not allow
one nurse to stay in the building on her own.
If all four stayed, the nurse would be able to
sit up with her husband; if not, she would
have to leave him.

"Sure then, you'd better stay the night," said
Doctor O'Flaherty, who was a friend of the
nuns. "Have my room, Sister, and I'll shake
down with one of the other doctors. I'll send
a message over to the Barrack for you—now
don't be worried in the slightest."

They were not worried. The break in routine made the evening a real picnic. The nurse stayed with her husband in the ward most of the time, so the three nuns were able to enjoy themselves in the doctor's room. Doctor O'Flaherty sent them in tea and food and a charcoal brasier which gave out so much smoke that they could hardly see one another. They talked and laughed all the evening. Sister Sarah thought she had never spent a gayer time since she joined her convent. She had been very lonely since her good friend Sister Elizabeth had been sent home. Most of the other Sellonites were elderly, and their rule did not encourage frivolity. They spent a great deal of time sitting alone, examining their consciences; good women though they were, their foundress' rule was too strict and too petty, so that many of them became thoroughly nervous cases. Sarah had seen one of them in floods of tears because her cap was starched a little too stiffly. Although she could not approve of the Roman religion, she preferred the unaffected cheerfulness of the Bermondsey Sisters.

They all laughed a great deal at very small jokes, and when they went to bed, Sister Sarah, who had tactfully made up her bed in the closet so that the two nuns could say their prayers together, left the door ajar so that she could hear them recite their evening office. Some of the psalms she knew, too, and as she joined in

the words, silently, she felt, as Sister Gonzaga
had felt, that surely there were more things to
hold people together than to keep them apart.

This unusual relaxation did all three of them
a lot of good, and the next day Sister Gonzaga
had almost forgotten her distress about the
Bishop's letter. It was brought back to her very
sharply, though.

In spite of having his own wife to look
after him, the nurse's husband died that day.
She was inconsolable. The amazing good for-
tune that of all the soldiers in the British army
only one, her husband, had been lucky enough
to have his own wife to nurse him, had made
her feel that heaven was on her side and God
could not intend him to die. So much had
gone right; now all had gone wrong, and she
could not believe it. She could hardly separate
herself from him when they came to take the
body away. She begged on her knees to be
allowed to go with him wherever they were
taking him. The poor woman almost had to be
restrained by force.

She came, then, sobbing as though her heart
would break, to Sister Gonzaga, who had been
particularly kind to her during the last few
days, and who seemed to have some sort of
authority even to those not of her own faith.

"We'll meet again in heaven, won't we, Sister?" she said through tears. "Tell me we'll

meet again in heaven. I couldn't bear to think I won't ever see him again."

Bishops may be wrong. They may be narrow-minded. But a nun is vowed to obedience. Sister Gonzaga's obedience was very sorely tried. It fought against common sense and sympathy and tolerance. But it won, though she longed with all her heart to take the poor woman's hand and comfort her with the thought of that meeting in heaven.

Obedience won, though victory seemed exactly like defeat. Sister Gonzaga struggled so hard that her voice was quite cold as she answered: "If we reach heaven, we shall see God there, and that should be enough for us."

One of the Protestant nurses, who happened to be within earshot, looked up in amazement. She had always believed that Catholicism was an unfeeling religion, and now she had proof. Sister Gonzaga saw the look and felt bitterly humiliated. The day had never seemed so hard or so long, and when she went back to the Barrack in the evening, for almost the first time she had nothing in the least cheerful to say to anybody.

Reverend Mother looked at her sharply, but said nothing. There were other matters to talk about, the most important being a change of plan which Miss Nightingale had made.

"You and Sister de Chantal are to come back

here to work, Sister. I am glad to say that Miss Nightingale has been able to find places for Reverend Mother Bridgeman's nuns. Five of them are to go to the General in your place, and they will have their own rooms and live there. The others are to go to a new hospital at Koulali, so we must hope that everyone will be happy about the new arrangements."

"I am happy, for one," said Sister de Chantal. "Life was a bit too easy for us, I think, and I'm glad to be working with you all again."

It was just as well that they were all working together again. At dinner a few days later, after the change had been made, Sister Stanislaus, whose looks had worried them all for some time, said she was sorry, but she really could not eat a mouthful. Her head was burning and she complained of thirst.

"Don't worry the doctor," she said through dry lips, when Reverend Mother had sent her off to bed. "He's worked off his feet and I'll be all right in the morning. I'm just tired, that's all."

The doctor did not come until the next day, by which time Sister Anastasia seemed to be suffering from the same thing. He looked at them both, and said briefly to Reverend Mother, "Typhus."

"Will you tell me what we should do?" she said in her usual calm voice.

"Yes," he said bitterly, "I'll tell you what you should do." He was young, and the sight of so much unnecessary suffering all around him—men dying like flies for want of simple medicines and simple nursing—had made him so helplessly furious that he had to work it off on somebody. "This disease, ma'am, depends entirely for its recovery on careful and constant nursing. Warm milk or broth should be given every hour and a half. If the fever rises too high, sponging with cold water, and ice applied to the head, have been found very soothing. Plenty of liquid should be given, as the patient will be intolerably thirsty."

Reverend Mother thought of the pint of water a day which was still their ration; she thought of the milkless tea, the tough, stringy meat, the sour doughy bread which were their only rations. She thought of the long hours that the patients would have to be left alone while the others worked in the wards. The nursing of thousands could not be interrupted for the sake of two.

"Thank you, doctor," she said.

CHAPTER NINE

Spring at Last

TYPHUS, OR JAIL FEVER, OR HOSPITAL FEVER, as it was called, because it spread so quickly wherever there was dirt and overcrowding, was the last of the epidemics to hit the Barrack Hospital, and it hit hard. February was perhaps the worst month of all the bad months. Everyone kept saying, "The spring *must* come soon. Things will be different in the spring," but it was a weary time to wait, and sometimes, in moments of depression, it seemed as though there would be no one left alive to welcome it when it did come. There was one awful week when there was only one doctor left on his feet.

It was not surprising that the two sick nuns had to be neglected, just as everyone had to be more or less neglected. Typhus is an alarming disease. The fever mounted and mounted for many days, and the others had to try to live and sleep in the same room in which the two women muttered deliriously. They cried for water all the time, and however much the others cut down their own supplies, it was not enough.

The young doctor saved them in the end. He went to Miss Nightingale with his report, and she knocked on the nuns' door a few minutes later. Reverend Mother opened it, for she tried to get back from her storeroom every hour or so for a few minutes to see what she could do for the patients.

"Reverend Mother," said Miss Nightingale reproachfully. At first she had felt angry, but she could not be angry when the only cause of it was too great a devotion to duty. "How could you keep silent? The doctor tells me I am to lose two of my best nurses and best friends because they cannot have proper care."

Reverend Mother looked at her from dark-circled eyes. She had hardly slept for days.

"They are no worse off than anyone else," she said.

"Well," said Miss Nightingale briskly, "I can spare two soldiers, but I cannot spare two nurses. They are more valuable to me and therefore we must look after them better." She spoke in an entirely professional manner, so that Reverend Mother would not argue. She stepped over to where the two sick nuns lay, their mattresses partly screened from the light by a bit of calico. No longer a friend, but merely the matron of the hospital, she listened to their breathing, took their pulses, felt the fever on their foreheads with the inside of her wrist.

"I am in charge of these cases," she said, "and these are my orders. You are to take whatever you need for them from my personal stores. And you are to use the extra kitchen at any hour of the day or night. I want reports on how they are getting on twice a day until the crisis of the fever is past. I will send someone to help you with the store duty so that you can nurse them properly. Warm milk with a dash of brandy or a few spoonfuls of beef tea should be given every hour. That should fetch them round the corner. And get barley water from Mrs. Clark—give them as much as they can drink."

She was gone before Reverend Mother could

speak her gratitude. When the two ward Sisters came back to dinner there was a very different feeling about the room. The helplessness was gone. Reverend Mother was busy with sauce-pans and spoons, carrying out her instructions and breathing prayers of thankfulness as she did so. Forty-eight hours later Sister Anastasia opened intelligent eyes and asked whether it was time for breakfast. Sister Stanislaus, who had been even nearer to death, and had in fact been anointed by the priest as she lay in a coma, was a little longer before she took a turn for the better, but for both of them the crisis passed favorably.

Not that getting back to health was easy. They needed constant nursing and feeding to give them back a little of the strength they had lost completely. Even more did they need constant cheering up, for the illness left them so low and depressed, particularly Sister Stan-islaus, that Reverend Mother wondered seri-ously whether they ought not to be sent back to England.

"It is so hard to be cheerful," said Sister Stanislaus wearily to Reverend Mother, "when we know that we are killing you with over-work."

"Another time you may have to nurse one of us, and you will be as happy to do it for us as we are to do it for you. The only way

you can reward us is by trying to recover as
quickly as you can. Look, the sun is shining
today. The spring is really coming, and all
sorts of things will be improved now. The
Government is sending out a sanitary commission. Miss Nightingale says they will arrive any
day now, and with orders to do anything that
they feel must be done for the good of the
hospital."

"I hope," said Sister Gonzaga drily, "that
they don't feel that they must pull the whole
place down. I think I should, if I were a sanitary commissioner, but it might be a bit uncomfortable for us."

"Tonight," said Sister Gonzaga to the invalids when she and the others came for their
tea the next evening, "we have each brought
you a piece of cheerful news. Things really are
improving. Sister de Chantal shall speak first,
as the youngest."

"And because my news is very mundane,
but very nice." She brought out a plate she
had been holding behind her, with five dark,
fat, delicious-looking Turkish sugar plums on
it. "This is today's ration; Miss Nightingale has
just given it to me. The Sultan has sent a huge
chest of Turkish candies 'for the ladies.' Turkish delight and all sorts of exotic-looking things.
Miss Nightingale said that it would be best to

portion them out every day for dessert, to make the army rations go down easier."

"My news goes no higher than the stomach either," said Sister Gonzaga, "but it is very cheering. Scutari Barrack Hospital, ladies, is to have a French chef!"

They thought it was one of her jokes.

"It's quite true," she said. "I forget his name, but he has been chef to one of the grand clubs in London, and he is coming out at his own expense because he wants to help Miss Nightingale and the army. He says that army rations need not be turned into pig swill for the men, and with everyone's blessing he is coming to show that the men can be decently fed."

They had to discuss this from every angle before they were ready to hear Reverend Mother's news. "Mine is quite a story," she said, "of which Sister Anastasia is the heroine."

"Who, me?" Sister Anastasia was astonished.

"Yes. You have done great good work without knowing it at all. Just before you fell ill you evidently had Colonel Paulet's orderly in your ward with fever."

"Yes," said Sister Anastasia, still looking so puzzled that the others had to laugh. "He was almost convalescent, the last I saw of him. I hope he was all right."

"He recovered very well, and the doctor said that it was entirely owing to your good nursing. So instead of an enemy we now have a firm ally, and there is no more talk of the nuns being turned out of the hospital."

This was good news indeed. Colonel Lord William Paulet was the new commandant who had taken Major Sillery's place. He had not been particularly sympathetic to Miss Nightingale and her nurses, and he had not been able to cope with the terrible situation in the hospital. Miss Nightingale said of him, "Lord William Paulet is appalled at the view of evils he has no idea what to do with . . . and then he shuts his eyes and hopes when he opens them he shall see something else." Needless to say, this attitude had not got anybody very far. Too weak to show proper authority over important things, Colonel Paulet had made up for it with a great show of putting his foot down over relatively unimportant ones. He had announced that he was sick and tired of the complaints of all the various religions about one another. Nurses, nuns, Sisters, chaplains, all seemed to be at loggerheads; Catholics, Anglicans, Presbyterians—most of them seemed much keener on what Miss Nightingale bitterly called "intriguing for their church" than on doing the job they were there for.

From all this the Bermondsey nuns had tried to keep free. They were perhaps almost the only people who kept unwaveringly to the promise which they had made before they came out, that they would not try to speak on the subject of religion except to members of their own church.

But things had got so bad, with Miss Nightingale almost distracted by the quarrels and stories and counter-stories, and the commandant so exasperated, that in the end he threatened to forbid anyone under his command to speak about religion at all.

This was very worrying to Reverend Mother. To be forbidden to say a prayer with a dying Catholic would turn the nuns into completely secular nurses, and this would be an impossible situation. She wrote for advice to the Bishop, and he told her that if the order was actually made in writing, she could not disobey it, but she would have to resign and bring her nuns home. That would seem like betraying poor Miss Nightingale, but of course the Bishop's order would have to be obeyed, and a great many fervent prayers were made over the linen stores and the bandages and the cans of soup that the choice would not have to be made.

Now, whether owing to Sister Anastasia and the commandant's orderly or not, the situation was saved, and that particular danger seemed to have disappeared.

March was altogether a more cheerful month

than February. The funny little Frenchman, Monsieur Soyer, arrived, bowing and waving his hands like everybody's idea of a comic Frenchman in a cartoon, but knowing his job and prepared to do it. He was soon firm friends with Miss Nightingale, for they recognized each other as people with the same ideas of efficiency.

Those in authority did not care for the way he wanted to turn things upside down, but M. Soyer cared nothing for their unfriendliness, for the Government at home had given him authority to carry out improvements.

He put an end, once and for all, to the system of boiling the rations, like washing, in huge copper vessels and sending them out to the men either half raw or stewed into strings. He trained cooks. He showed them how to make soups and stews. He invented ovens to bake good bread and biscuits instead of the almost uneatable Turkish stuff. He invented a huge teapot which held tea for fifty men and, better still, delivered it to them boiling hot.

No wonder that the wards received him with three cheers whenever he visited them.

Almost at the same time came the sanitary commission to see what could be done with the Barrack Hospital and why so many men died in it and why it smelled so appalling. The theory that disease was spread by germs and viruses had yet to be discovered, but people knew that dirt and bad air spread infection, and although the dirt had to a certain extent been conquered since Miss Nightingale came, the air was still so sickening that visitors to the place were frequently ill for days after breathing it for a few minutes.

"It is impossible," said Miss Nightingale later, "to describe the state of the atmosphere of the Barrack Hospital at night. I have been well acquainted with the dwellings of the worst parts of most of the great cities of Europe, but have never been in any atmosphere which I could compare with it."

The sanitary commissioners hired Turkish workmen and started on the good work. The divans which ran around each room were pulled out, making hundreds of rats homeless. When the rats were killed, one source of disease was checked.

Then the water supply was dug up and found to be mixed up with the drainage. Among other treasures, they found the carcass of a dead horse in the drinking water.

Most important, the sewage system, which had been bad when it was put in, and had been getting worse ever since, was remade. The pipes were rotten, the cesspools too small. No wonder the air had been bad; the whole hospital

had been almost floating on a lake of its own
sewage.

Of course, things were not righted immediately. It took time. But as soon as the work
was begun the death rate began to fall, and by
May Miss Nightingale felt that things were
well enough in hand for her to start on the
next task. She would go up to the Crimea itself, to Balaclava, where the hospitals were reported to be in an extremely bad way too, and
see what order she could bring out of that
chaos.

No one liked to see her go from Scutari, but
the very fact that she *had* gone made them
realize how much better things were. The sun
shone; convalescents were able to stroll out of
doors and pick wild crocuses to bring in for
their friends who were still too ill to get up.
Everything seemed bright and hopeful for the
first time.

It was a lovely May afternoon when the bad
news came. Sister Gonzaga was on duty. A
transport had come in the day before with
some sick men from Balaclava, and for almost
the first time their reception was thoroughly
satisfactory. Nothing was makeshift; no one
was neglected.

The men had been carried up from the jetty,
given baths, had their hair cut and their dirty
clothes exchanged for clean nightshirts. They

had been put into clean beds. The doctor had seen all of them, and given orders for whatever food or medicine was suitable, and these things were forthcoming. Sister Gonzaga was giving a man his broth and thinking about these things when an orderly came in, very hoarse and quite pale.

"She's sick," he said, and no one had to ask who "she" was. "She's down with the fever in Balaclava and they don't think she'll live."

The man turned his head away from Sister Gonzaga's spoon and took no more interest in his broth. A strange hush hung over the hospital as the news spread. Everywhere men turned their faces to the wall so that others should not see their tears. There was not one of them, even those who had never actually seen her, who did not feel that if Miss Nightingale died he would have lost a mother.

Balaclava

CHAPTER TEN

The End of the War

REVEREND MOTHER SAT IN THE GARDEN ON A chair which the faithful Vickery had brought her. It was the garden of the little wooden house they called Sabin Place because it used to belong to Mr. Sabin, the chief Protestant chaplain. He had been invalided home in 1855 and had given the house to Miss Nightingale because it was so conveniently near to the Barrack Hospital.

It had first been used as a convalescent home

for Miss Nightingale herself, when she had been slowly recovering from the Crimean fever, and then as a rest house for the nurses.

There was not much of a garden, but to sit under the one tree, now fresh and green with its spring leaves, was a change for anyone who had hardly moved outside the Barrack for sixteen months.

"Will you be all right now, Reverend Mother?" said Vickery anxiously.

"Yes, thank you. You must go back. The Sisters will come to fetch me on their afternoon walk."

He saluted and left, and Reverend Mother folded her hands and looked at the wilderness of weeds and nettles in front of her. A few hens scuffled for food, and a suspicious-looking cat watched this invader of its private territory.

"Tib, Tib, Tib," said Reverend Mother kindly.

But it was evidently a Turkish cat and not used to familiarity from foreigners. It switched its tail and disappeared.

It was very peaceful just to sit and let one's mind rove over the past year and a half, and to thank God quietly for the bad times and the good times, and the wonderful way in which even the worst of things had been turned into blessings. For she could see blessings in almost everything, and never more so than during this

bad illness, which had brought her very close
to God and more at peace then ever.

The war was over. Eight days ago the news
had arrived, and there had been tremendous
salvos of guns from the ships in harbor and
the troops on shore. The Sultan of Turkey had
come over to Scutari to the British camp for a
grand review of troops. It was not only a
hospital base now. There was a great camp
both of infantry and cavalry, and from the
hospital they could hear the bugles blowing,
until they became quite clever at recognizing
the calls.

The Sisters, with Vickery as escort, had
climbed the tower to see the review. Theirs
was probably the best grandstand view of the
occasion. They had come back and described
the uniforms and the splendor of it all to Reverend Mother, for at that time she was still too
weak to leave her room. She had tried once to
get to Mass, but it had not been a success,
and she had had to be helped back again, rather
ashamed of herself for being a nuisance.

Now it was April 10th, 1856, and the war
was really over. Of course the actual decla-
ration of peace had not meant as much as it
might have, because there had been very little
fighting for six months, ever since the fall of
Sevastopol. It had taken the Great Powers a
very long time to agree among themselves

about the peace, and it would take still longer
to tidy things up and get all the men and the
equipment home again.

She took out a letter and began to reread it.
It was from Miss Nightingale, at the moment
up at Balaclava with three of the Bermondsey
nuns. Reverend Mother would have been up
there too, had not first dysentery and then
pleurisy attacked and nearly killed her.

"Dearest Reverend Mother,
Your precious health is the chief of my
cares. I beseech you to go to Malta with Sister M. Gonzaga or Sister M. Anastasia or
both, if it were only for two or three weeks,
when Dr. Cruikshank recommends it. Please do
not neglect his advice or I shall be obliged to
come back to tyrannize over you. . . . Your
Sisters here are perfectly well, very efficient
and very cheerful."

They had need of cheerfulness, for things
in the Crimea were being made very difficult.
Reverend Mother wished that she could be
with them. Even after all that had happened,
the dislike of some of the medical authorities
for Miss Nightingale was very bitter, and of
course, as had happened before, her faithful
Bermondsey nuns came in for a share of the
bitterness, which even included threatening
letters.

Some of the hard-boiled old medical officers had not words bad enough to describe Miss Nightingale, and unfortunately they had on their side Reverend Mother Bridgeman and the Irish nuns. They were prepared to admit that "The Bird" had done some good at Scutari, in the black months, but that was no reason for allowing her to get too big for her boots and order them all about, now.

They fought with her, and encouraged her nurses to be rebellious, and sent confidential reports with false stories about her to the Government at home. They circulated stupid and unpleasant tales, such as that Miss Nightingale had a three-course dinner prepared for her every day by M. Soyer, while the nurses starved on stringy ration beef. They said that she used the faithful Mrs. Roberts, her right-hand nurse, as a private lady's maid. It was fantastic that people could be got to believe anything of the kind, but when people want to believe, they find no difficulty in doing so, and they are able to delude themselves very successfully.

The "anti-Nightingale" group was particularly strong in the Crimea, and when she went up there to try to make the hospitals as efficient as she had at last made the Turkish ones, such petty jealousies made her life and the lives of her Bermondsey nuns a misery. But they, as

Miss Nightingale reported to Reverend Mother, were "very cheerful and used to being abused."

Reverend Mother felt no anger against such people. She could always find it in her heart to forgive, but she looked forward eagerly to the day when the doctors would allow her to go up to the Crimea too (she had not the slightest intention of going to Malta on leave while there was work to be done) to work and suffer beside her Sisters.

Not that Miss Nightingale said more than she could help about the suffering in her letters. She did not want to trouble the invalid too much. And always her letters were full of kind anxiety.

"It is the greatest consolation I could have to hear that you are better. I beseech you to take all the means which are recommended for the recovery of your health and to remember how valuable your life is to this poor world. I do not say this because I think that life can be very valuable to you in it—but because we cannot spare you yet. Have you changed your room?

"I want my cardinal very much up here—but I do not mean to have her till you are quite well."

Reverend Mother read no more for the present. Even that slight effort tired her very much. She sat and looked at the towers of the Barrack Hospital, just visible over the surrounding houses.

The Barrack was a very different place now. The past had faded like a nightmare. There were naturally no more wounded, and very few sick patients of any kind. Now the staff catered mostly to accidentally broken bones and crushed limbs, bad burns from explosions, and so on. But there were not many of these, and the number of sick lessened all the time. The British army was in better shape than it had ever been.

If only the lessons so bitterly learned would last, Reverend Mother thought with a sigh. For this fine army was not the same army. The first one had died in the winter of 1854–55. Twenty thousand men had died, and only one in ten of wounds—the others from cholera, scurvy, starvation, frostbite, dysentery, typhus. And yet, she had heard, the French had lost as many and the Russians thousands more.

Others beside the soldiers had died. Nurses, doctors and chaplains had gone too in those ghastly months of January and February, when the living could not raise enough strength to bury the dead, and the Turks had carted the bodies from the hospital in dozens, to tip them into shallow pits without decency or reverence.

The nursing staff had suffered. One of the

Sellonites had been invalided home. Three of
the paid nurses had died of fever, some had
had to be sent away for bad conduct, some had
been too worn out and been honorably sent
home on medical grounds. One of Mother
Bridgeman's nuns was buried up at Balaclava.
Some of the nurses had been lost in a more
amusing way. One day six of them had come
to Miss Nightingale's office in an embarrassed
bunch, leaving six gallant corporals and ser-
geants outside the door as moral support, and
asked permission to get married!

In fact, of all the original groups of nurses,
only the Bermondsey nuns were still together.
And they had had several narrow escapes. First
there had been the typhus, in which they had
so nearly lost two of their number. But Sister
Anastasia and Sister Stanislaus (the latter now
up at Balaclava, cheerfully coping with insults,
short rations, rats, cold and dirt) were more
than fully recovered.

Then it was Miss Nightingale they had
nearly lost. The long winter had taken toll of
her so that when she caught the fever on her
first visit to Balaclava it had been a complete
collapse and she had very nearly died. For-
tunately Mrs. Roberts had been with her at
the time, and she had made a slow recovery.

After some weeks she was brought back to
Scutari, to this little house, to convalesce.

Nothing showed what the soldiers thought of her better than the way in which anxious crowds of them had followed her stretcher, in absolute silence.

She had recovered, at least partly, and gone back to work. Then summer came, and it was hot and dry, and everyone was exhausted. There were fewer nurses and the tower was not so crowded; the Bermondsey nuns were given the room at the top with all the windows, but it was not much cooler, and they were plagued by mosquitoes. They had to get out of bed two or three times a night to catch the creatures whenever they heard that peevish zing-zing above their heads in the dark.

Reverend Mother and Sister Anastasia proved to be the most skillful hunters, and Sister Gonzaga, in her usual fashion, made the most of their efforts when she wrote letters home. In fact, during all these months she had been the life of them all, as well as having become a superb nurse, one of the best three with the expedition. They all did their best, and there was little to choose between them, but Sister Gonzaga seemed to have that extra touch of intuition which is a pure gift. Besides, her gaiety never flagged. Her letters were so amusing that the Sisters in Bermondsey might have thought that life at Scutari was one long picnic. All her letters were decorated around the

edges with pictures. Sometimes it was cartoons
of the nuns in characteristic attitudes—the five
of them meekly trailing to Mass behind the
chaplain, or the way Sister Stanislaus doubled
herself up when she wrote a letter so that her
face disappeared under her veil. Sometimes it
was Mrs. Bracebridge in her Sunday cap, or a
row of whiskered soldiers singing the hymns at
Benediction; or her fancy was caught by the
sight of the sergeant serving Sunday Mass—an
enormous man who had been issued a coat
several sizes too small; or she was tickled by
the all-too-common sight of a very drunk private being carted off to the cells by four
others.

But then, in the summer, quite suddenly, the
reaction had come. Perhaps these days we would
call it a nervous breakdown. Whatever it was,
for three long months Sister Gonzaga was sick
in mind and body—nervous, moody, unable to
eat or sleep, miserable with herself and her
own failure, haunted by the pictures of the
awful times they had been through, worrying
them all with her depression, which she seemed
unable to shake off. If it had been only a
physical illness, rest would have cured it. If
it had been only a mental one, work would
have done wonders. But the two together made
a vicious circle, so that she could do nothing
except brood, and this made her worse.

She was so bad that the hospital doctors almost sent her home. Perhaps it was this threat that cured her. Something did, and once she began to get better she recovered as quickly as she had sickened. She was soon back in the wards again and entirely her old cheerful efficient self.

So the five were still together, though they were no longer five, but eight.

Over and over again, almost from the first week they arrived, Miss Nightingale had wished she could have more Bermondsey nuns. At last she got her way. Sister Helen, Sister Martha and Sister Joseph had come out in the January of 1856, when the nursing strength of the expedition had begun to run low. At this moment it was two of them, and Sister Stanislaus, who were over in the Crimea with Miss Nightingale, Mrs. Roberts, and two other very good nurses.

Reverend Mother looked up to see Sister Gonzaga and Sister Joseph coming through the garden. She was glad to see them, for even sitting for half an hour had tired her, and she would be glad to get home and rest.

They walked back, very slowly. It was only a few hundred yards to the Barrack, but it was far enough for someone who had almost died a couple of weeks before.

"We met Vickery," said Sister Gonzaga. "I

think if he had had his way he would have
sent up a stretcher for you."

Vickery was Reverend Mother's devoted
slave. At one time he had gone back to his
regiment and had written them long letters
from the Crimea, telling them all the news of
the front line. But after the fall of Sevastopol
he had come back to the hospital with a wound
in his arm and an extra stripe on his tunic. The
wound had long since healed, but Vickery was
permanently an orderly sergeant now, and
nothing, it seemed, was going to shift him from
Scutari as long as Reverend Mother and the
nuns were there.

There were many huts now on the piece of
waste land between the two hospitals. It looked
very different from the old days. Sister Gonzaga amused Sister Joseph by telling her about
their daily walks across it, up to the ankles in
mud, and sometimes fighting off the wild dogs
with their umbrellas.

There was one of the largest huts at which
they looked with special interest. The men
called it "The Inkerman Coffee House." It
was a club room for the soldiers which Miss
Nightingale had started.

"You are spoiling the brutes," the Scutari
commandant had growled to her when she first
suggested it. But she had insisted that if one
gave the soldiers a place where they could buy

coffee and borrow books, and play chess and
write letters quietly, they would use it, and it
would save many of them from going to get
drunk out of sheer boredom.

Quite a lot of people had been astonished by
the plan, and still more astonished when it
worked.

"Of course it worked," said Reverend
Mother. "She has made people understand that
if you treat soldiers like men, and good men,
they will behave like men, and not like
animals."

They stopped again by the Turkish ceme-
tery at the top of the hill. It was a pretty spot,
with its pointed cypress trees and its grave-
stones. The men's were marked by a carved
red fez, the women's by a sort of plume, and
you could tell which were the children's, for
they were graduated in size according to the
age of the dead person, so that a baby's grave
was marked by a pathetically tiny stone.
Beyond the graveyard was the glorious view
which was always worth another look—across
the Bosphorus. And there almost below them
was the jetty at which they had all landed.

"Do you remember the day we came?" said
Sister Mary Joseph. "Father Duffy had been
so kind to us all the way, but he left us sitting
in the caique while he went up to the hospital
to say that we had arrived. And there we

stayed, not daring to land, and with everyone staring at us. We were so frightened of the Turks, and then we were dreadfully in the way because a funeral was coming past and we were sitting just where they wanted to land the coffins. Oh, dear! And then Vickery arrived, and you, Reverend Mother, to rescue us. We were never so grateful to see anyone."

"Oh, dear yes. I had been looking out of the linen store window for days, and wishing you would come, and then a soldier burst in that afternoon to say that you were there. Vickery was so cross to think you'd been left there alone, and he went striding down that hill. I don't know how I managed to keep up with him. And there you were, looking so forlorn and unhappy, poor dears."

"I think we had better go in," said Sister Gonzaga. "You must be getting tired, Reverend Mother."

The next day two letters from Miss Nightingale arrived, begging for the other three Sisters to come at once. This would leave only Reverend Mother, who was not fit for work, and Sister Gonzaga, who not only had to look after Reverend Mother but was needed to run the extra kitchen, and who now, as the senior nurse in the hospital, took on Miss Nightingale's old job of making the night rounds.

The troubles in the Crimea had reached a

pitch, with the result that Reverend Mother
Bridgeman had packed up and left with all
her nuns—a serious loss as far as nursing staff
went, for they had been excellent nurses. But
those first old quarrels had never been patched
up, and there had always been difficulties and
disagreements. It is difficult now to hand out
blame for such things; no doubt it was on
both sides as blame usually is, and it sprang
almost certainly from the fact that these two
strong-willed women had very different ideas
of the work they were doing. However that
may be, the "Reverend Mother Brickbat," as
Miss Nightingale always referred to her, and
her fourteen nuns, sailed away in a huff. Miss
Nightingale was relieved in some ways, but
very short-handed, so she sent the SOS to Scutari for the three Bermondsey nuns.

The letters came at midday, and almost at
the same time came a message from the ship's
captain that he was sailing back at three o'clock
and passengers would have to be aboard before
then.

Sister Gonzaga whisked around doing the
packing while the Sisters got themselves ready,
went for a last visit to the chapel (they had a
real chapel now in the hospital, with the Blessed
Sacrament always there), and Reverend Mother
sat down to write to Miss Nightingale and the
Sisters.

Miss Nightingale's letters to her were full of praise for the three Sisters already there, and as affectionate as ever.

"Our Sisters," she wrote, "are quite well and cheerful and most efficient and useful. Dr. Taylor expressed to me yesterday in the strongest words his feeling of the reform they had worked in his L.T.C. Hospital. They do more than medicine, he said. . . .

"Dear Reverend Mother, I hope that whatever you determine upon" (Miss Nightingale had been trying for some time to persuade her to take sick leave in Malta until she was quite strong again) "you will do no work at Scutari; a slight imprudence might have such consequences. I have begged my Aunt to let me know if you begin to work or to do anything imprudent. And if you do, you know I must come back. Your life is the most precious thing we have, both for the work's sake and for the Community, and to peril it for the sake of C Store, or for any Store, would break our hearts."

Two hours later, the boat set sail and Reverend Mother and Sister Gonzaga found themselves alone. It was a very strange feeling and at first they were quite miserable, but the letters that came from the Crimea after a few days cheered them up. There were still troublesome and annoying people, but to offset this, there were others who did everything in their power to show the Sisters how welcome they were. As had happened all along, to the true Christians differences of religion meant nothing when it was a question of showing kindness, and one of the best friends the Bermondsey nuns found at Balaclava was Mr. Holt, the Protestant chaplain.

He came to them with presents of eggs when rations were short (one of the petty annoyances the authorities thought up was to be childishly difficult about the nurses' rations), and they answered this by offering to wash and iron his white parson's bands.

"I hope you'll remember to mention this in confession," he said jokingly to Sister Mary Joseph. "I'm sure that doing a Protestant's laundry must be a serious thing."

And he quite often managed it so that he happened to be about when the Sisters were getting into the carriage which took them between the hospitals, which were a long way apart. On these occasions he opened the carriage door for them, bareheaded, so that anyone who cared to notice could see that he, at least, the chief representative of the Protestant Church, had the highest esteem for these Catholic ladies.

They cared very little for misunderstandings, anyway, so long as they felt that they were doing the right thing, and the right thing was, as it always had been, their loyal service to Miss Nightingale in whatever she asked them to do.

Their only worry, a very real one, was the state of Reverend Mother's health, for no one was very hopeful that she would go away to Malta for a rest, as Miss Nightingale had been advising in every letter.

The solution came suddenly and unexpectedly, however. One of the priests, knowing that Reverend Mother's loyalty to the service could be overcome only in one way, had already privately written home to Bishop Grant, and his orders came by return mail, not to be ignored. There was nothing to do but to catch the next ship home, and Sister Gonzaga would have to go too, as Reverend Mother could not travel alone, and she was the only Sister left at Scutari.

It was all done so hurriedly that the *Victoria* had already sailed before this sad letter arrived at Balaclava to break the news. Obedience always came first with Mother Mary Clare, and she would not have had it otherwise, but it was heartbreaking to have to leave her children, her work, and the Superintendent to whom she had been the loyalest friend.

"Dearest Children," she wrote, "You will see by the Bishop's letter to Miss Nightingale, which she will show you, that I am obliged to return to Bermondsey, and perhaps on Monday, April 28th.

"It is indeed a painful separation but we know it is best to do God's Will and we know it to be His Holy Will since it is the direction of our Superior. Yet what I do feel intensely is being unable to see you dear Sisters and our dear good friend Miss Nightingale. . . .

"I need not tell you my wishes, dear Children, you know them. Be united and happy and cheerful and humble, loving God and trusting in His care, without a shadow of mistrust and asking our dear Blessed Lady to show herself a Mother to you in all things and then if you make some mistakes have no anxiety; you may be sure our Blessed Lord will not allow you to do anything contrary to His honour and glory.

"Now I will only add, be good and faithful, work away merrily, and what a hearty welcome I shall have for you all when you come home to dear Bermondsey, which might be much sooner than we imagine."

CHAPTER ELEVEN

Homecoming

"Reverend Mother," said Sister Gonzaga the next day, "may Vickery come in? He has something very particular to ask you."

Reverend Mother looked up from her account books. She had finished her farewell letters, and now she was busy making sure that everything was left in perfect order for the next storekeeper. She could not help feeling both sad and amused to find how she disliked the thought of anyone else's taking over the stores and the linen rooms that she had cared for during all these months.

"Of course Vickery may come in," she said.

Vickery was twisting his forage cap around in his hands.

"If you please, Reverend Mother," he said, "it's this. Would you just let me take you over the water for a bit of an outing this afternoon? You can't go away home to England and never see Constantinople at all. It's a beautiful place and it would be a crying shame, indeed it would."

"Well," said Reverend Mother, "I don't see why not, do you, Sister? I'm sure we can think of some good reason why we ought to go."

"Of course there are good reasons," said Sister Gonzaga. "We'll think of them as we go along, shall we?"

So shortly afterwards they were sitting in a caique, side by side, dancing over the water to glittering Constantinople, with Vickery sitting on the opposite seat, respectful and excited.

It was, as Vickery said, a beautiful place. They were enchanted by the bazaar with its rows of little shops, where men not only sold things but frequently made them as well, so that you could peer into dark booths and hear the clink of silversmith's hammers, or the clicking of the looms. It was all color and brightness with patches of deep shadow. Veiled Turkish women looked at them curiously, but the men sat stolidly smoking their pipes outside the shops and looked as if an earthquake could not shake their Eastern calm. There were soldiers of all the nationalities swaggering in the streets, and sometimes Vickery had to push a way for them past caravans of minute donkeys with overhanging loads.

It was easy enough to think of good reasons for doing some shopping, and Vickery was soon burdened with some odd-shaped parcels. There was a length of lovely silk to make a frontal for the Lady altar at Bermondsey, a Turkish pipe for the sexton who was always so kind to them (this was Sister Gonzaga's idea; she was tickled at the thought of old Jack solemnly puffing a chibouk like a Turk), and a pair of fine candlesticks as a present to the 88th, which was stationed at Scutari. This regiment, the Connaught Rangers, being Irish and almost entirely Catholic, had always been favorites of the nuns, and the nuns of them. They had done wonders in erecting a chapel and furnishing it. Bishop Grant and the Bermondsey convent had given them most of the necessary things for it, and the candlesticks would be the finishing touch of grandeur.

They finished the afternoon by calling on the Sisters of Charity, who had always been kind, and the Superior gave them some rosaries which she had brought back from Jerusalem.

Monday came all too soon, though the parting was so sad that in a way it would be a relief to have it over and be actually on their way.

They could see the ship from the hospital windows, a huge screw steamer with two funnels and four masts. It was reputed to be a fast ship, and they were told that the voyage should take only two weeks to London, if they were lucky.

"All invalids on board at ten o'clock," the doctor said briskly, but Vickery had other ideas.

"Indeed you will not go at that hour," he said. "There's no need at all. I shall take you down myself this afternoon and it will be quite soon enough. I'm going down first to see that all's well, and I'll come for you after dinner."

So there was time for the two nuns to walk the wards of the Barrack Hospital for the very last time. They hardly spoke to each other on the way, because each of them was remembering the same things. Many of the wards were empty. In the others a few men lay in clean white beds, their faces shaved, their hair neatly cut. The long passages were passages again. The floors were scrubbed, the walls whitewashed. Over all hung the clean

smell of soap and carbolic. But without mean-
ing to, Reverend Mother and Sister Gonzaga
walked slowly down the exact middle of the
empty corridors, as though they were avoiding
the feet of wounded men who lay on sacks of
straw.

At three o'clock that afternoon they went
on board, with quite a crowd of people.
Everyone who was left at the hospital was determined to see them off in style.

Vickery had been as good as his word.
There was a comfortable double cabin for
them, with two bunks and a long locker which
could do for a sofa, and a pile of oranges to
last the trip. What kind of threats, promises or
bribes Vickery had used on the bedroom steward no one knew, but the man was as attentive
and polite as though they were the only passengers he had to look after.

It was all very different from the voyage
out.

At half past five the steamer made the
echoes of the Bosphorus ring with her hooter.
Then the screw began to thresh and throb and
slowly she pulled away from the anchorage and
headed out to sea.

The deck was full of invalided officers and
men, doctors, a troop of Artillery ordered
home, even some of the soldiers' wives and
children. But none of them gazed backwards as

intently as the two nuns standing by themselves in the stern. They had no eyes for the glittering city of Constantinople, but stared and stared at the great square Barrack Hospital high above the houses of Scutari.

Sister Gonzaga was the first to speak. With a great sigh she dismissed the most eventful year and a half of her life.

"I do hope," she said, as they turned to go down below, for it was high time that Reverend Mother had some rest, "that we can go ashore at Malta. After all this time and all that has happened, I would like to hear Mass again in the church of St. John." . . .

Their reception at Bermondsey did not take place until eighteen days after they sailed from Scutari, for the weather was nearly as bad as on their first trip, and they were delayed. This time they were both ill, at least to begin with, but they had recovered by the time they reached Malta, and were indeed able to go to Mass in the great church at Valetta.

"I'm really very happy to see Malta *without* Mr. Bracebridge," said Sister Gonzaga.

No one noticed the two inconspicuous nuns who landed at Portsmouth and took the morning train to London. Their fellow passengers glanced at them once or twice, perhaps wondering a little about the religious habit. If they had been recognized for what they were, the red carpets would have been spread all the way from Portsmouth to George Row, for the Crimean nurses were the darlings of England.

And then, there was dear Bermondsey, and such a welcome! Nobody knew whether to laugh or cry, with pleasure at welcoming them home, and distress to see Reverend Mother looking so tired and thin and worn. Their first visit was to the chapel, and then Reverend Mother was ordered away to her room to have some rest.

Waiting for her was a letter with the familiar army postmark from Balaclava, written the day the *Victoria* left Constantinople, the same day that Miss Nightingale had heard the news of her being ordered home, and had sat down to try and pour out on paper all that Reverend Mother had meant to her during the months at Scutari.

"My dearest Reverend Mother,
     Your going home is the greatest blow I have had yet; but God's blessing and my love and gratitude go with you as you well know.

"You know well too that I shall do everything I can for the Sisters whom you have left me. But it will not be like you. Your wishes shall be our law and I shall try and remain in the Crimea for their sakes as long as any of us are here.

"I do not presume to express praise or gratitude to you, Revd. Mother, because it would look as if I thought you had done the work not unto God, but unto me. You were far above me in fitness for the General Superintendency, both in worldly talent of administration and far more in the spiritual qualifications which God values in a Superior. My being placed over you in our unenviable reign in the East was my misfortune and not my fault.

"I will ask you to forgive me for everything or anything which I may, unintentionally, have done which can ever have given you pain, remembering only that I have always felt what I have just expressed, and that it has given me more pain to reign over you, than to you to serve under me. . . .

"Dearest Reverend Mother, what you have done for the work, no one can ever say, but God rewards you for it with Himself. . . .

"Will you ask one of the Sisters at home (I dare say Sister M. Gonzaga will do so) to write to me about your health?

"And believe me, whether I return to see you again in this world or not,

"Ever my dearest Reverend Mother's
      gratefully, lovingly, overflowingly,
            Florence Nightingale."

CHAPTER TWELVE

The Work Will Go On

MISS NIGHTINGALE WAS THE LAST OF THE "Female Nursing Establishment" to leave Scutari. She traveled home with her aunt, Mrs. Smith, who had been with her out there ever since Mrs. Bracebridge had left the year before. Some of the people in the boat bound for Marseilles must have known that the slim youngish lady in black was the famous Miss Nightingale, but they pretended that they did not. She called herself Miss Smith and stayed in her cabin most of the voyage. She was sick, and very tired, and she did not want to be recognized.

The whole of England was on tenterhooks to give her a grand reception. The mayors of Folkestone and Dover had been trying to find out at which of their ports she was likely to land so that there could be a public reception. They wanted to have triumphal arches, and military bands, and banners saying "Welcome to Miss Nightingale," and fireworks and speeches. All three regiments of Guards would have liked to line the streets to play her home with fanfares, and skirling pipes, and tremendous brass bands. Any soldier in the British army would have been proud and happy to have presented arms to her. They would rather have honored her than the Queen herself. The village where her parents lived wanted her to arrive in a carriage so that they could take the horses out and pull her up to the house in a joyful procession.

She did not want any of this.

"Oh, my poor men," was all she could think. "I am a bad mother to come home and leave you in your Crimean graves."

Now that the work was over, the picture of Scutari in the bad months haunted her. It was all she could think of, even in her sleep. There was only one place where she wanted to

be welcomed—Bermondsey, where they would
understand what she felt because they had been
through it all with her.

Everyone was home at Bermondsey now. In
July Sister Mary Helen, Sister Joseph, and Sister Martha had come back, leaving the three
old hands to finish off the work in the hospitals. A fortnight later they too came, having
traveled in a sick transport. They had nursed
the men all the way, so that it was really with
their arrival at Portsmouth that the work of
the "Nursing Establishment" came to an end,
just as it had been their departure from London Bridge which had been the beginning of
it all.

They had reached Bermondsey to find that
Reverend Mother was away. She had been sent,
again by the Bishop's orders, which was the
only way to make her take any step which was
for her own good, to a convent in France, at
Boulogne. Again Sister Gonzaga had gone with
her, and there for three weeks they breathed
sea air and did nothing very much. For of
course Reverend Mother could not rest in
Bermondsey. Her long absence, during which
the convent had been so very short-handed,
meant that there was a tremendous amount of
business to be done, and the only way to stop
her from doing it was to send her away.

While they were away, a most exciting letter

had reached them from the Bishop. A committee of Catholic gentlemen had started a plan to found a new hospital in London. It would be the first Catholic hospital founded in England since the Reformation, although of course they did not mean it to be for the use of Catholics only. They wanted, and the Bishop agreed with them, some way of using all the nursing experience gained by the nuns during the war. They would found and maintain the hospital if the Bermondsey Sisters would staff it.

Reverend Mother, looking thoughtfully at Sister Mary Gonzaga's shining face as she read the letter, and hearing her eager discussion of the subject afterwards, thought to herself that with the Bishop's permission she knew where to find the first Reverend Mother of that new hospital.

A few days later Sister Gonzaga received a last letter with the Scutari postmark, written just before Miss Nightingale sailed.

"You do not give me a good account of her," Miss Nightingale wrote anxiously. "Do not write again for I shall soon be home now.

"I shall not stop in London at all, but go to Bermondsey to call upon Reverend Mother, and then sneak quietly out of the way. . . .

"Dear Cardinal Gonzaga, this comes with best love from

Your poor old Pope."

This would have been a good reason for going home at once from Boulogne, and in any case Reverend Mother was anxious to finish her holiday. It would soon be the annual retreat at the convent, and she longed to be there for that. She sometimes felt that she had got so behindhand with her prayers during the hospital days that she would never catch up again. She quite understood that other people had not had much time to pray when they were so busy, but she could not help feeling that she had often been idle. Somehow, she had wasted a great deal of time, and time was not hers to waste; it was God's.

On the second morning of the retreat, the brass bell on the convent doorpost pealed at eight o'clock in the morning. It was Miss Nightingale, alone. She had managed to reach England without being noticed. The nuns welcomed her and took her in as though she were one of themselves.

She was not a Christian of any particular denomination. She did not much mind in what kind of a church she prayed to the God Who was very important to her. Someone had said of her that she belonged to the sect which is unfortunately a very rare one, the sect of the Good Samaritan.

But she had a particular reverence for the Catholic Church when it was represented by people like Reverend Mother Mary Clare and Dr. Manning, who was afterwards the Cardinal. When she went to the Crimea she took only three personal papers in a little black pocket-book. One was a letter from her mother; one was a rather bitter little farewell note from the man who had hoped to marry her, but whom she had given up for the sake of her nursing work; one was from Dr. Manning commending her to the protection, worship and imitation of the Sacred Heart.

She did not feel in the least strange, there-fore, to be kneeling in the convent chapel at Bermondsey, praying in the company of the nuns who had meant so much to her. And they were very happy to have her with them.

The altar lamp glowed just as it had on the evening in October two years before, when they had made up their minds to volunteer for the expedition to the Crimea. If they could have looked ahead then they might have been terrified. If they could have looked ahead now, far enough ahead, they would have seen very thankfully an enormous amount of good which sprang from that first decision.

The first thing they would have seen, for it was only a few months away, and the plans were already laid, was the foundation of the Hospital of St. Elizabeth, which afterwards be-came the Hospital of St. John and St. Elizabeth, which still flourishes in London, and is still staffed by the same Order that founded it. They would have seen it starting in a rather old house and then, much later, moving to splendid new buildings in a quieter part of the city, where it still is. It was opened on November 19th, 1856, with a staff of five nuns, four of them veterans of Scutari, headed by Sister Mary Gonzaga.

The beginning was typical of the Bermondsey nuns. The day before the hospital opened, they all went, Reverend Mother Clare with them, and scrubbed the floors. There were only twelve beds, which had cost five pounds each, and nothing much else.

The Cardinal came to bless it next day, looked around the wild patch of garden, and drove off in his carriage, to come back shortly afterwards with a supply of garden tools as a present to the community. It was a special sort of hospital, for women and children with diseases that were either incurable or would take a very long treatment—the kind of people that the ordinary hospitals in those days had neither space nor time for.

Here Sister Gonzaga, Sister Helen, Sister Stanislaus, and Sister Anastasia all worked, and they must have been particularly pleased when it was taken under the protection of the

Knights of St. John of Jerusalem, and they were allowed to wear the Maltese cross embroidered on their habits. It was the mother church of this Order that they had visited at Malta on that well-remembered day when Mr. Bracebridge had marched them around on their sight-seeing tour.

They would have had to look a long way ahead to see the end of the Crimean Sisters' work. In the year of Queen Victoria's Jubilee, 1897, there were still four of them alive. Sister Mary Stanislaus, Sister de Chantal, Sister Helen, and Sister Anastasia were then summoned to Windsor to receive the Royal Red Cross from the old Queen. They met there at least one Sister from Norwood, and one of Mother Bridgeman's nuns, who were also decorated.

Sister Mary Stanislaus did not die until 1913, nearly sixty years after the Crimean War, and Miss Nightingale lived nearly as long, after spending her life working for soldiers and for nurses. Many people forget, knowing only the story of those two terrible years, that most of her work was done afterwards.

She never forgot her Scutari friends, and the Hospital of St. John and St. Elizabeth still keeps among its treasures a note scribbled when she was already old and sick:

"My dear Sister Stanislaus,

Life is too busy for both of us to look back upon the Crimea much. But when I think of it I always look back upon you, dearest Sister, in the little General Hospital at Balaclava.

"And dear, dear Revd. Mother at Scutari, now a Saint in Heaven."

For Sister Mary Gonzaga and Reverend Mother Mary Clare had been the first of the band to go, although not for a good many busy years after the end of the war.

Reverend Mother spent all the rest of her life at Bermondsey, and died there a very holy and peaceful death. The last words she said, very slowly and clearly, were:

"We must give an account of our talents."

VISION BOOKS

All Vision Books have full color jackets; black and white illustrations, sturdy full cloth bindings. Imprimatur.

Vision Books

4484